NEW EDITION

McDougal Littell

Math*Thematics*

Teacher's Resource Book

MODULE 1 Search and Rescue

MODULE 2 Bright Ideas

D1411151

BOOK 2

McDougal Littell

A DIVISION OF HOUGHTON MIFFLIN COMPANY

Evanston, Illinois • Boston • Dallas

Acknowledgments

Writers

The authors of *Math Thematics, Books 1–3*, wish to thank the following writers for their contributions to the *Teacher's Resource Books* for the *Math Thematics* program: **Lyle Anderson, Mary Buck, Roslyn Denny, Jean Howard, Deb Johnson, Sallie Morse, Patrick Runkel, Thomas Sanders-Garrett, Bonnie Spence, Christine Tuckerman.**

Image Credits

Photography
Front Cover © Cedar Point, Sandusky, Ohio.

Illustration
2-4 Jeremy Spiegel/McDougal Littell/Houghton Mifflin Co.

All other art by McDougal Littell/Houghton Mifflin Co.

THE STEM PROJECT *McDougal Littell Math Thematics®* is based on the field-test versions of The STEM Project curriculum. The STEM Project was supported in part by the

 NATIONAL SCIENCE FOUNDATION

under Grant No. ESI-0137682. Opinions expressed in *McDougal Littell Math Thematics®* are those of the authors and not necessarily those of the National Science Foundation.

ISBN-13: 978-0-547-00115-9
ISBN-10: 0-547-00115-0

123456789–BHV–11 10 09 08 07

Contents

    A blackline master of the Pre-Course Test from the student textbook

    Module 1 Diagnostic Test, *The Math Gazette*, Assessment Scales, Warm-Up Exercises, Labsheets, Practice and Applications, Study Guide and Exercises, Quick Quizzes, Solution to Textbook E^2, Format for an E^2 Solution along with Sample Scoring Profiles and Sample Student Solutions, Mid-Module Quiz, Module 1 Tests, Standardized Test, and Performance Assessment

    Module 2 Diagnostic Test, *The Math Gazette*, Assessment Scales, Warm-Up Exercises, Labsheets, Practice and Applications, Study Guide and Exercises, Quick Quizzes, Solution to Textbook E^2, Alternate E^2 and Solution, Mid-Module Quiz, Module 2 Tests, Standardized Test, and Performance Assessment

About the Teacher's Resource Book

In conjunction with the *Math Thematics*, Book 2, Teacher's Edition, this Resource Book contains all of the teaching support that you need to teach Modules 1 and 2.

Math Thematics Overview

The first Resource Book for each level includes the following course overview materials:

Teaching with *Math Thematics* A detailed explanation of the sections in the student textbook, the planning support in the Teacher's Edition, and the teaching resources in the Teacher's Resource Books.

Assessment in *Math Thematics* A description of the various forms of assessment available to the teacher in the student textbook, in the Teacher's Edition, and in the Teacher's Resource Books. Includes a detailed discussion of the use of Assessment Scales in this program, and suggestions for creating portfolios.

Teacher's Scavenger Hunt A scavenger hunt through the *Math Thematics* program's components to help teachers become more familiar with all the resources available to them.

Literature Connections A list of literature excerpts used in *Math Thematics*, Book 2.

Materials List A list of materials needed for use with Labsheets, Explorations, and Exercises in *Math Thematics*, Book 2.

Blackline Masters

The teaching support in the Resource Books is organized by module and section and includes the following materials:

Warm-Up Exercises Each Warm-Up page is printed in large easy-to-read type and can be used to create an overhead visual or used as a hand-out. Answers for the exercises are provided at the bottom of the page.

Labsheets Blackline masters used in conjunction with various Exploration questions to present data and extend the scope of the Exploration. Answers are provided in the Teacher's Edition.

Practice and Applications One to two pages of additional practice for each section in a module, as well as combined practice that covers the whole module.

Study Guide Two to three pages of Study Guide for each section of the module. These Study Guide pages feature key concepts, worked-out examples, and exercises. They can be used for review and reteaching.

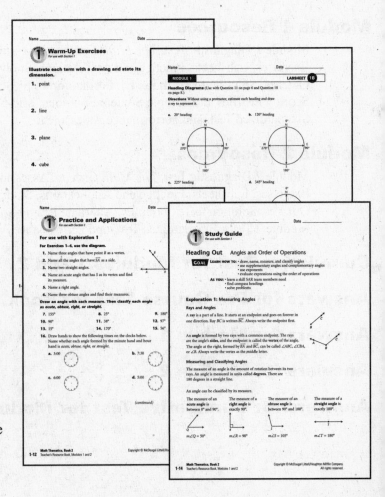

Extended Exploration (E²) Solution Guide

A comprehensive discussion of the Extended Exploration in the student textbook, including how to assess student responses and performance.

Alternate Extended Exploration (Alternate E²)

Included in the Teacher's Resource Books for Modules 2, 4, 6, and 7, these extended explorations can be substituted for ones in the student textbook. Materials include teaching notes and assessment procedures.

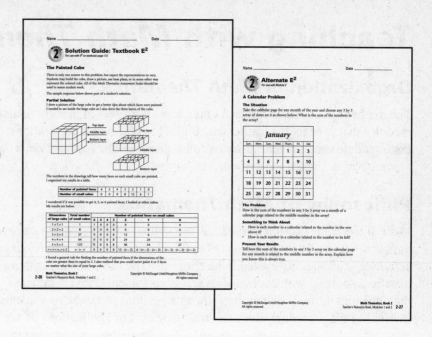

Assessment

Assessment options include a diagnostic module pre-test, quick quizzes for each section, a mid-module quiz, and two module tests, Forms A and B.

Cumulative Test

A cumulative test on both the modules of this Resource Book.

Module Standardized Test

A page of standardized multiple-choice questions for each module.

Module Performance Assessment

A Performance Assessment Task for each module.

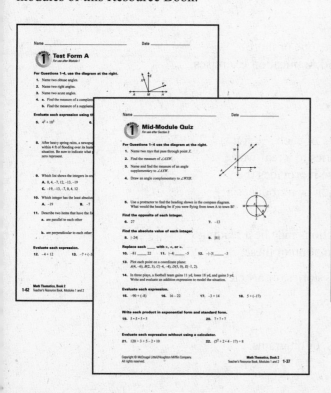

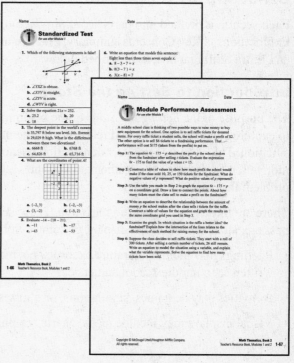

Answers

Complete answers to Practice and Applications, Study Guide, Quick Quizzes, and all Assessments for both modules are provided at the back of this Resource Book.

Teaching with *Math Thematics*

Organization of *Math Thematics*

The mathematics content for each grade level is presented in eight thematic modules that connect the mathematical ideas to real-world applications. Each module contains four to six sections, an *Extended Exploration*, a *Module Project*, and a *Review and Assessment*.

Philosophy of *Math Thematics*

Most of the *Math Thematics* materials are written so that students discover the mathematics. Through the use of manipulatives, models, and hands-on activities, students actively learn the concepts. The rules and algorithms usually associated with mathematics are often student-derived, rather than given in the text. Explaining why an algorithm works helps students internalize the procedure. Because some concepts or applications do not lend themselves to discovery learning, direct instruction is also used in *Math Thematics*.

It will be important for you, as a teacher, to work through many of the questions in the Explorations and Exercises. Because of the interactive nature of this curriculum, it is important for teachers to be aware of the possible questions their students might ask and of the problems they might encounter.

Close-Up of a Section

Each section is divided into parts: a *Setting the Stage*, one or more Explorations, a Key Concepts summary, Practice and Application Exercises, and Extra Skill Practice, as described below.

Introduction to *Setting the Stage*

The purpose of the *Setting the Stage* at the beginning of each section is to capture students' interest and relate the mathematics to a real-world situation. This is an integral part of a section because it provides the motivation for learning the mathematics of the section or introduces a problem that will be explored.

There are three types of *Setting the Stage*. These sections may be a reading passage, an activity, a visual display, or some combination of these.

- Readings may include literature excerpts, poems, stories, or articles written for a middle school audience.

- Activities may be games, simulations, or quizzes.

- Visual displays may include maps, charts, graphs, or diagrams.

Each *Setting the Stage* includes *Think About It* questions, which help deepen the student's understanding of what he or she has read, done, or seen. The questions range from simple recall to application. Often, students intuitively explore an idea in the *Think About It* questions that they will later investigate in depth.

Introduction to an Exploration

After the *Setting the Stage*, each section contains one to three Explorations where students are actively involved in learning new mathematical content. Each Exploration requires one class period, and, depending on the nature of the activity, may be completed by students working individually, in small groups, or as a whole class. The activities in the Explorations range from guided discovery to open-ended investigations. Students investigate a question or problem by doing one or more of the following:

- Collecting, generating, researching, and presenting data
- Using concrete and/or visual models
- Applying problem solving strategies
- Looking for patterns and relationships
- Exploring alternative methods and solutions
- Using number sense
- Applying prior knowledge.

The Explorations provide opportunities for students to observe, analyze, predict, make and test conjectures, and communicate their ideas orally and in writing.

Goals, Key Terms, and *Set Up*

Each Exploration and some *Setting the Stage* sections begin with a *Goal* and may include a list of *Key Terms* and a *Set Up*, if appropriate.

- The Goal statements give a summary of the mathematics being covered.

- The Key Terms list important vocabulary being introduced in the Exploration and can serve as an advanced organizer for students who need it.

- Both students and teachers should read the Set Up, which lists the most appropriate class set up—whole class, small groups, or individual—as well as any materials needed for the activity. The materials listed may include Labsheets, which are used in conjunction with various Exploration questions to present data and extend the scope of the Exploration. The Labsheets are available in the Teacher's Resource Books (as blackline masters) and in the Student Workbook. Labsheets may also be used with many exercises, and with the Extended Explorations, Module Project, and Review and Assessment pages.

Exploration Questions

Communicating about and through mathematics, both orally and in writing, is embedded throughout the *Math Thematics* curriculum.

- Discussion questions provide opportunities for students to check their understanding of a concept by sharing or generating ideas with others. The questions can be explored in pairs, in groups of four, or as a class.

- Try This as a Class questions are designed to bring the class together to develop an algorithm, pull ideas together, pool data, or complete a more challenging problem.

- Checkpoint questions are provided as a way to quickly assess whether students understand the mathematics.

Student Support Notes

- Side notes accompany Checkpoints to remind students what they have been learning.

- Each Exploration concludes with a list of Homework Exercises related to the content of that Exploration.

- For Help boxes in Explorations and elsewhere refer students to the module where a concept was first learned or to the Toolbox or Tables at the back of the textbook.

Introduction to *Key Concepts*

Students can use the *Key Concepts* to review for a test or as a reference when they have missed a day of class. The *Key Concepts* are also a resource for parents who are helping their child with homework.

Key Concept pages can be helpful in the following ways:

- Giving a quick overview of content
- Illustrating the content with examples
- Highlighting the most important content
- Listing the new vocabulary in the section, and
- Providing a reference to applicable pages in the Exploration.

The *Key Concept Question* reinforces the ideas from the section, often pulling the content of all the Explorations in the section together.

Introduction to *Practice and Application Exercises*

The questions in the *Practice and Application Exercises* include skill level, application, single-answer, open-ended, and critical thinking questions. A wide variety of topics are covered in these exercises. Students may explore how the content relates to other areas of mathematics, other subjects, or different cultures.

- The Teacher's Edition provides a guide to using many of these exercises as embedded assessment items.

- The Reflecting on the Section questions can also be used to assess student learning.

- The Spiral Review exercises revisit topics from previous sections in the module as well as concepts from previous modules. They may also review material mastered at a prior grade level. They are carefully planned to provide an ongoing schedule of practice to help students master content and prepare students for upcoming sections by reviewing prerequisite skills.

Some sections may include these questions:

- A Career Connection, a set of application-based exercises about people who use mathematics in their career

- Extension problems that challenge students to extend what they have learned and apply it in a new setting.

Introduction to *Extra Skill Practice*

The first half of the *Extra Skill Practice* reinforces the concepts students investigated in the Explorations of the section. The exercises are usually at a skill level but sometimes are application-based.

The bottom half of the page focuses on *Study Skills* in some sections and *Standardized Testing* in other sections.

- Study Skills questions explore how students learn (visual, auditory, or kinesthetic), how to take notes, and how the text is organized.

- Standardized Testing questions help students become comfortable with various formats of standardized testing questions using the mathematical content of the section.

Organization of the *Teacher's Edition*

The *Teacher's Edition* provides suggestions at *point of use* for helping students understand new concepts and avoid common errors. Other features include classroom examples, classroom management ideas, and ideas for differentiating instruction.

Complete planning support is provided by module and section planning guides that include mathematical overviews and teaching strategies, day-by-day planning guides, and suggested homework assignments. The *Teacher's Edition* also includes professional articles and resources available for each section, including technology resources. See the *Teacher's Edition*, pages T35 and T36–T47.

Organization of the *Teacher's Resource Books*

Teaching resources are presented in four *Teacher's Resource Books* at each grade level, with each Resource Book containing materials for two modules. These resources are organized by section to make it easy for teachers to find the materials available for that section. The *Teacher's Resource Books* contain a variety of resources for each module:

- Teaching tools, including section warm-up exercises, labsheets, additional practice and application exercises, study guide materials, and parent newsletters

- Assessment tools, including section and mid-module quizzes, module diagnostic pre-tests, module tests, standardized tests, module performance assessments, cumulative tests, and pre-course, mid-year, and end-of-year tests

- Answers, including answers for all Resource Book materials for the two modules and any cumulative tests in that Resource Book.

See the descriptions of each of these resource types on pages TR-4 and TR-5 in this *Teacher's Resource Book for Modules 1 and 2*.

The information on pages TR-11–TR-25 describes the Assessment component in the *Math Thematics* program. After reviewing these materials, you may want to take the Teacher's Scavenger Hunt on pages TR-26 and TR-27 to help you become more familiar with how to use all the components of the *Math Thematics*, Book 2 program. (Answers are provided.)

Assessment in *Math Thematics*

Introduction

Assessment, by which we mean all the procedures used to collect information on any aspect of the teaching and learning process, is an integral component of the *Math Thematics* curriculum.

The assessment component in *Math Thematics* provides a guidance system—a guidance system for teachers, for parents, and most importantly, for students.

Purposes of Assessment

The primary purpose of assessment is to improve learning. To achieve this goal, the *Math Thematics* assessment component is designed to be an integral part of the instructional process, rather than an add-on to it. Not only is assessment information drawn from instructional tasks, but the assessment tools themselves are designed to help students master concepts and develop skills.

The *Math Thematics* assessment component serves four major purposes:

- Monitoring student progress in problem solving, reasoning, and communication

A major goal of the *Math Thematics* curriculum is to develop each student's ability to solve problems, reason logically, and communicate ideas effectively. Making problem solving, reasoning, and communication a primary focus of assessment conveys the message that these are valued skills. But more importantly, the scales used for *Teacher Assessment* and *Student Self-Assessment* provide dynamic tools for helping students learn

what they can do to improve in these areas.

- Assessing student proficiency in content areas

Assessment data are used to document students' understanding of mathematical content and processes, and to determine whether students have achieved the learner outcomes of the *Math Thematics* curriculum. The data are derived from multiple sources using a broad range of mathematical tasks.

- Helping teachers make instructional decisions

The assessment tools provide information teachers can use to decide what instruction is necessary to help students achieve the outcomes of the *Math Thematics* curriculum. The results of ongoing assessment may indicate a variety of needs such as reteaching concepts, reviewing or practicing skills, or presenting additional material using a different model or teaching technique.

- Documenting student progress for students, parents, and teachers

Assessment is about more than grades, but teachers are usually expected to translate assessment data into grades. Samples of student work gathered during assessment can provide an objective basis for determining student performance levels. Having a portfolio containing examples of a student's work can show growth over time. By comparing examples in the portfolio, you can clearly communicate to the student, parents, and other teachers the indicators of excel-

lent work (A), good progress (B), developing concepts and skills (C), and minimally acceptable work (D).

Assessment Tools

The following assessment tools are incorporated into the *Math Thematics* curriculum. (See also the Summary of Assessment on pages T30–T31 in the *Teacher's Edition*.)

Warm-Ups

Warm-Ups are short activities found in the *Teacher's Resource Books* that provide systematic review of concepts and skills. *Warm-Ups* can be photocopied for the class or projected with an overhead. They are often used for pre-assessment purposes to determine whether students have the prerequisite skills or knowledge for a section.

Embedded Questions

Because assessment in *Math Thematics* is an integral part of instruction, many assessment items are embedded in the instructional materials.

Discussion questions provide opportunities for students to check their understanding of a concept by sharing or generating ideas within their group or as a class. Mastery of the concept is not expected at this point, but teachers should monitor the discussions to check for misconceptions that may need to be corrected.

Checkpoints are questions or problems that are used by the teacher to check understanding of a concept or skill before students continue with the exploration. *Checkpoints* appear after students have explored a concept and when some level of mastery is expected. If students are not able to complete the problems correctly, re-teaching may be necessary.

Try This as a Class questions appear at points where direct instruction is needed to summarize key ideas or to bring closure to a line of inquiry. They are similar to *Discussion* questions, except that the teacher directs the discussion or activity and guides the learning. Not all *Try This as a Class* questions are used for assessment. Some are simply used to demonstrate a procedure or to pool data.

Some *Practice & Application Exercises* are designed to be used to assess whether students have learned specific concepts, procedures, and processes. These exercises, which may be used for instructional decision making and grading, are identified in the *Teacher's Edition* as embedded assessment exercises. They range from straightforward applications of concepts and procedures to open-ended questions that require students to recognize the appropriate mathematical content, choose an effective approach, and construct a response.

Reflecting on the Section exercises provide an opportunity for students to look back on the section as a whole and refine, describe, summarize, or extend the mathematical ideas they have explored. A *Reflecting* exercise may take the form of a *Discussion, Research, Oral Report, Journal,* or *Visual Thinking* question. Writing or talking about a concept helps students solidify their understanding of it. It may also help them make connec-

tions to other subject areas or among mathematical concepts. Students' responses to the *Reflecting* exercises should be considered for inclusion in their portfolios.

Extended Explorations (E^2s)

E^2s are extended problem solving activities. They are typically open-ended problems that apply a variety of mathematical concepts and may be solved in different ways. The solution often involves constructing a mathematical model for the situation. To solve the problem, students must define the problem, devise and carry out a plan for solving it, and prepare a presentation in which they explain and interpret their solution. Each E^2 may be assigned for completion in about a week's time. The solution is assessed using the *Teacher Assessment Scales* and *Student Self-Assessment Scales*. Solutions to some E^2s should be included in students' portfolios to document growth in problem solving, reasoning, and communication.

A sample Solution Guide for the textbook E^2 is provided in the *Teacher's Resource Book* for each module. In addition, Alternate Extended Explorations and their solutions are provided in the *Teacher's Resource Books* for Modules 2, 4, 6, and 7.

(For more information on *Managing Extended Explorations*, see the article on pages T44–T45 in the *Teacher's Edition*. For help with assessing E^2 solutions, see the Format for an E^2 Solution, sample Scoring Profiles, and sample Student Solutions materials on pages 1-39 to 1-42 in this *Teacher's Resource Book for Module 1*.)

Module Projects

Each module contains a *Modu[le] Project* that provides an oppor[tu]nity for students to apply mat[h]ematical concepts as they lear[n] them. The project is related to the theme of the module, but [it] may also require mathematica[l] knowledge from earlier modul[es.] Questions and activities in the *Module Project* relate to the mathematical concepts taugh[t] in the module. Students prepa[re] a report or presentation to co[m]plete the project. Some *Modu[le] Projects* should be included in students' portfolios to demonstrate their understanding of mathematical concepts as wel[l as] their ability to apply them.

Module Review and Assessmen[t]

Each module concludes with [a] set of questions that can be u[sed] to review and assess the conte[nt] of the module. Additional asse[ss]ment materials are provided i[n] each of the *Teacher's Resource Books*. These include mid-mod[ule] quizzes, module tests, Standa[rd]ized Tests and Module Performance Assessments.

Portfolios

A student portfolio is a collecti[on] of representative samples of th[e] student's work. It may include such things as assignments, answers to *Reflecting on the Section* exercises, solutions to *E[2s]* and *Module Projects*. Its purpos[e] is to provide comprehensive documentation of the student['s] progress in, attitude toward, a[nd] understanding of mathematics over a period of time.

Using the *Math Thematics Assessment Scales*

About the *Math Thematics Assessment Scales*

The *Math Thematics Assessment Scales* are designed to help students answer the question "How can I improve my performance in problem solving, reasoning, and communications?" They provide a generalized rubric that defines the various dimensions of mathematical investigation. The scales are designed to be applied to open-ended questions, *Module Projects, Reflecting on the Section* exercises, and especially *Extended Explorations* (E^2s). Students are encouraged to write their solutions to these items using appropriate mathematical language and representations to communicate how they solved the problem, the decisions they made as they solved it, and any connections they made. Their work is assessed using five scales:

- Problem Solving
- Mathematical Language
- Representations
- Connections
- Presentation

The key to improving student performance is to actively involve them in assessing their own work. This is achieved through use of the *Student Self-Assessment Scales*. As students become familiar with the scales, they understand what they need to do to improve their problem solving, reasoning, and communication.

Teachers assess students' work using the same scales written from a teacher's point of view. The combination of student and teacher assessment provides important feedback to help students improve.

If used consistently, the *Math Thematics Assessment Scales* have the potential to raise the level of students' performance. However, you and your students will not master the use of the *Math Thematics Assessment Scales* immediately. This is okay—the more work you and your students assess, the better and the more comfortable you will be with the assessment process.

As you work with the *Math Thematics Assessment Scales*, keep the following in mind:

- The scales are a powerful way for both you and your students to look at work.
- Learning to use the scales is like learning a new language. It requires time and patience.
- Students' higher-order thinking skills will improve as a result of using the *Math Thematics Assessment Scales*.
- Be flexible!

A copy of all the scales can be found on page 1-6 (*Teacher Assessment Scales*) and on page 1-7 (*Student Self-Assessment Scales*) in this *Teacher's Resource Book*. The scales are repeated in the Resource Book for each module. The *Student Self-Assessment Scales* also appear on page 113 in the student textbook.

The following are descriptions of each scale.

The Problem Solving Scale

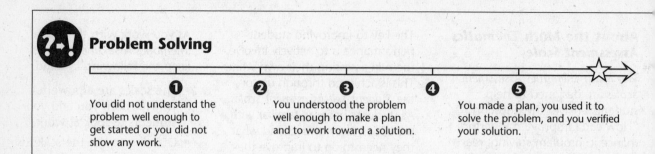

Problem Solving

❶ You did not understand the problem well enough to get started or you did not show any work.

❷ You understood the problem well enough to make a plan and to work toward a solution.

❸

❹

❺ You made a plan, you used it to solve the problem, and you verified your solution.

The *Problem Solving Scale* assesses the student's ability to select and use appropriate mathematical concepts and problem solving strategies (guess and check, make a model, look for a pattern, and so on) to solve a problem. The scale emphasizes and reinforces the steps in the *4-Step Approach to Solving Problems*—Understand the Problem, Make a Plan, Carry Out the Plan, and Look Back.

The *Teacher Assessment Scale* shown above gives the range of the criteria used to assess a student's work for problem solving. The following descriptions expand on the criteria.

Level 5: The student's approach worked and led to a correct solution.

The following are characteristics of a Level 5 solution:

- All the relevant information was used to solve the problem.
- The problem solving strategies, procedures, and mathematical concepts used were appropriate for the problem and were carried out completely.

- When strategies were only partially useful, the approach was modified successfully.
- The solution was checked for reasonableness.
- Other possible solutions were explored.
- The solution was verified through the use of a second approach or with a clear explanation of how the approach actually solved the problem.

Level 3: The student was able to make progress toward a solution.

The following are characteristics of a Level 3 solution:

- A workable plan was used, but the solution is incomplete or only solves part of the problem.
- The problem was only partially solved because some of the relevant data were not used.
- The mathematical procedures and problem solving strategies used were appropriate for the problem, but they were not carried out completely or they did not lead to a complete solution.

- The mathematical concepts chosen were appropriate but only partially solved the problem.

Level 1: The student did not understand the problem well enough to get started on a solution or did not show any work.

The following are characteristics of a Level 1 solution:

- There was no apparent plan for solving the problem or the solution was not related to the problem.
- Information was misinterpreted or irrelevant data were used.
- Problem solving strategies were used randomly or were not used at all.
- Incorrect or inappropriate mathematical procedures were used.
- The mathematical concepts chosen were not appropriate for the problem.

Levels 2 and 4 may be used to show performance that falls between the described levels. For example, a student may have used an appropriate approach and found a correct solution to the problem, but then stopped without checking the reasonableness of the solution or trying to verify it. This solution might be scored at Level 4 rather than Level 5. Similarly, a solution that has some of the characteristics of a Level 1 solution and some of a Level 3 solution might be scored at Level 2. The Star (☆) Level should only be used to indicate exceptional work.

The score on a scale is shown by filling it in with a marker up to the level number.

Questions Students Ask About the *Problem Solving Scale*

What is meant by a solution?

A solution includes your answer and all the work you did to get it. Sometimes it may be necessary to include an explanation of your approach and why you chose it.

What if I make a computation error? How does that affect my score?

The goal in problem solving is always to find an accurate solution, so you should make it a habit to check your work carefully. It is still possible, however, to get an incorrect answer because of a minor computational error. Depending on how serious the

error is, this may lower your score one level on the *Problem Solving Scale*. The error will be noted at the bottom of the assessment sheet.

What does it mean to "verify my solution"?

The most common way to verify a solution is to solve it another way. For example, you could solve the problem using different problem solving strategies or a different approach and show that you get the same answer. Another way to verify your solution is by clearly explaining your plan and showing that it effectively solved the problem.

The Mathematical Language Scale

Mathematical Language

1 You did not use any mathematical vocabulary or symbols, or you did not use them correctly, or your use was not appropriate.

2

3 You used appropriate mathematical language, but the way it was used was not always correct or other terms and symbols were needed.

4

5 You used mathematical language that was correct and appropriate to make your meaning clear.

The *Mathematical Language Scale* assesses the student's use of mathematical vocabulary, notation, and symbols. The scale encourages consistent and accurate use of mathematical language.

Level 5: The student used mathematical language correctly and consistently. The language used was appropriate for the problem and it helped to simplify or clarify the solution.

The following are characteristics of a Level 5 solution:

- The mathematical language used was appropriate for the problem.

- The mathematical vocabulary and symbols were used consistently and accurately.

- The use of mathematical terms and symbols helped to communicate the solution.

Level 3: The student used appropriate mathematical vocabulary and symbols, but the usage was not always correct or additional terms and symbols could have been used to simplify the solution or make it clearer.

The following are characteristics of a Level 3 solution:

- The mathematical vocabulary and symbols chosen were appropriate for the problem but more could have been used.

- Appropriate mathematical terms and symbols were used, but they were not used consistently or there were minor errors in usage.

Level 1: The student did not use mathematical vocabulary or notation in the solution, or the terms and symbols used were inappropriate or used incorrectly.

The following are characteristics of a Level 1 solution:

- The use of mathematical terms and symbols the student should know would have helped to simplify or to clarify the solution, but none were used.

- Inappropriate mathematical language was used.

- Mathematical terms or symbols were used incorrectly or imprecisely.

Questions Students Ask About the *Mathematical Language Scale*

What is appropriate mathematical language?

You are using appropriate mathematical language if the terms and symbols you are using help to simplify your solution or to make it clearer. Using extraneous terms or symbols that do not relate to the problem or aid in the solution is inappropriate.

Does one mistake in language lower my score?

Usually, one error would not lower your score, especially if the other terms and symbols you used were appropriate and were used correctly.

The Representations Scale

 Representations

❶ ❷ ❸ ❹ ❺ ⭐➡

❶ You did not use any representations such as equations, tables, graphs, or diagrams to help solve the problem or explain your solution.

❸ You made appropriate representations to help solve the problem or help you explain your solution, but they were not always correct or other representations were needed.

❺ You used appropriate and correct representations to solve the problem or explain your solution.

The *Representations Scale* assesses the student's use of graphs, tables, models, diagrams, and equations to solve problems. The *Representations Scale* looks specifically at whether the representations are accurate and appropriate.

Level 5: The student used representations that were accurate and appropriate for the problem. The representations helped to solve the problem or explain the solution.

The following are characteristics of a Level 5 solution:

- The representations used were appropriate for the problem.

- The representations helped to solve the problem or to communicate the solution.

- The representations were correct and accurate.

Level 3: The student used representations that were appropriate for the problem, but they were not always accurate or correct, and other representations could have been used to simplify the solution or to make it clearer.

The following are characteristics of a Level 3 solution:

- The representations used were appropriate for the problem, but additional representations were needed to solve the problem or to help communicate the solution.

- The representations were appropriate, but there were some errors in constructing or using the representations.

Level 1: The student did not use representations to help solve the problem or to explain the solution.

The following are characteristics of a Level 1 solution:

- The use of representations would have helped solve the problem or clarify the solution, but none were used.

- The representations used were inappropriate for the problem and did not help solve it or explain the solution.

Questions Students Ask About the *Representations Scale*

What makes a representation appropriate?

To be appropriate, a representation must accurately represent relevant information in the problem or help to organize the information. The representation should actually solve or help to solve the problem. For example, suppose the data in a problem could be displayed in a circle graph, but the graph does not solve the problem or give you a clue about how to solve it. Then it is inappropriate.

What makes a representation accurate?

A graph is accurate if the axes are labeled, the graph displays data that are relevant to the problem, the data are plotted accurately, the graph is titled correctly, and, if necessary, an accurate key is provided. A table, chart, diagram, or model is accurate if it is correctly labeled, it is well organized, and it accurately reflects information relevant to the problem.

The Connections Scale

Connections

①	**②**	**③**	**④**	**⑤**

① You attempted or solved the problem and then stopped.

② **③** You found patterns and used them to extend the solution to other cases, or you recognized that this problem relates to other problems, mathematical ideas, or applications.

④ **⑤** You extended the ideas in the solution to the general case, or you showed how this problem relates to other problems, mathematical ideas, or applications.

The *Connections Scale* assesses the student's ability to make connections within mathematics, to real-world situations, and to other disciplines. This scale emphasizes and reinforces the Look Back step in the *4-Step Approach to Solving Problems*.

This is the most difficult scale for students to understand and use. Because they often have limited mathematical knowledge and virtually no experience making connections, students' initial connections will be limited to recalling similar problems, finding and extending patterns, and relating the math to their everyday lives. To help students grow in this area, it is extremely important to continually encourage them and prompt them to look for and to make connections.

When extending solutions to the general case, many students lack the skills to express the general rule algebraically. Their extensions will involve descriptions of the patterns they found and may include a verbal rule. This is particularly true for sixth grade students. As students mature, their ability to use algebraic notation should increase, and they should become comfortable using it.

Level 5: The student generalized the solution or showed how the problem is related to other problems, mathematical ideas, or applications.

The following are characteristics of a Level 5 solution:

- The solution was extended to the general case.

- The solution was applied or interpreted in a real-world situation.

- The student clearly demonstrated how the problem is related to another mathematical concept or to another problem.

Level 3: The student recognized patterns and was able to use them to extend the solution to other cases of the same problem or recognized that the problem is related to other mathematical ideas, problems, or applications.

The following are characteristics of a Level 3 solution:

- The student found patterns that led to the solution but did not generalize the solution.

- The solution was extended to other cases of the same problem.

- Alternative solutions were explored.

- The student recognized that the problem is related to other problems, mathematic concepts, or applications but did not explain or illustrate the connection.

Level 1: The student solved the problem and stopped without looking back to see how the solution might be extended or generalized or how the problem relates to other problems, content, or applications.

The following are characteristics of a Level 1 solution:

- There are connections that the student should have recognized, but none were mentioned or explained in the solution.

- The solution does not indicate that the student looked for patterns that might be generalized.

- Alternative solutions were not recognized or were not pursued.

- The problem was not check or examined from a different perspective.

Questions Students Ask About the *Connections Scale*

What does it mean to extend my solution?

After you have solved a problem, you can extend it in many ways. One way is to solve the problem for different cases. For example, suppose a problem asked you to find the number of handshakes that would occur when five people shook hands exactly once. If you solved the problem for five people and then found the number of handshakes for six, seven, and eight people too, you have extended the solution. Another way to extend a problem is to write a general rule that can be used to find the number of handshakes for any number of people.

In Levels 3 and 5 on the Connections Scale, *what is the difference between recognizing that the problem relates to other problems, mathematical ideas, or*

applications and showing that it does?

When you first begin making connections, you will discover that problems are related to other problems, mathematics, or applications. You might say "this is just like the handshake problem." In this case, you recognized the connection. When you show the connection, you will clearly link the problem, mathematics, or application with an explanation.

The Presentation Scale

 Presentation

❶ The presentation of your solution and reasoning is unclear to others.

❷ **❸** The presentation of your solution and reasoning is clear in most places, but others may have trouble understanding parts of it.

❹ **❺** The presentation of your solution and reasoning is clear and can be understood by others.

The *Presentation Scale* assesses the student's ability to reason logically and to communicate ideas effectively. This scale assesses why students did what they did to solve the problem. Evidence of reasoning is shown by making and testing conjectures, formulating models, explaining why, and gathering and presenting evidence. The differences between levels on the scale reflect both the correctness and the clarity of reasoning.

Level 5: The presentation clearly explains what the student did, why it was done, and how it solved the problem.

The following are characteristics of a Level 5 solution:

- The student's work was clear and focused. The details presented fit together and made sense.

- The presentation was well organized. One step followed from another.

- Strong supporting arguments were presented.

- All the important aspects of the problem and the relevant data were identified.

- Examples and counter-examples were included where appropriate.

- The solution is such that any-one who reads it will follow what was done, why it was done, and how the solution was obtained.

Level 3: The presentation explains what the student did and why it was done, but parts of the explanation are incorrect or are not clear.

The following are characteristics of a Level 3 solution:

- There is either an explanation or a clear inference of appropriate reasoning in the solution.

- Almost all of the reasoning is correct, but some of it may be unclear.

- There is evidence that unsuitable methods and incorrect solutions were eliminated.

Level 1: The presentation does not clearly explain or demonstrate what the student did or why it was done.

The following are characteristics of a Level 1 solution:

- The solution does not solve the question that was asked.

- There is no evidence of reasoned decision-making in the solution, or the solution indicates the possibility of reasoned decision-making, but the reader cannot be sure.

- The solution was organized in a haphazard or disjointed manner.

- The reasoning was incorrect

- The solution does not contain an explanation of what was done and why, or the explanation is not understandable

Questions Students Ask About the *Presentation Scale*

What does it mean to clearly explain my reasoning?

You must explain how you arrived at your solution and why you took each step you did. For example, if a student joined our class today and read your solution, would that student understand what you did and why you did it?

Do I always have to tell in words why I did what I did in order to score high on this scale?

It is possible that your work is organized so clearly that your reasoning can be inferred. However, it is helpful for you to explain what you did and why you did it. Some people think more clearly when they write things out, so writing helps them to clarify the situation and their thoughts.

About the *Math Thematics Assessment Scales*

Questions Teachers Ask About the *Assessment Scales*

What if the student and I do not agree on the assessment?

This is an excellent opportunity to discuss the differences between the assessments with the student. Comparing and contrasting the teacher and student assessments provides an important feedback loop that will lead to improved problem solving, reasoning, and communication.

Can the Math Thematics Assessment Scales *be used to assess problems that were solved as a group?*

Yes. Individual accountability is very important to the success of cooperative learning. So even if students work in a group to solve a problem, they should document the work individually. This individual documentation can be assessed using the assessment scales.

How can I tell if an exercise should be assessed with the Math Thematics Assessment Scales*?*

All *Extended Explorations* should be assessed using the assessment scales. Additional exercises that can be assessed with the scales are identified in the *Teacher's Edition.*

Will all the problems allow a student to score at the highest level on each scale?

No. Some problems have greater potential for certain scales than others. Sometimes students may not even be scored on a scale because the problem does not elicit the criteria for that scale.

If a problem is not scored on a scale, how will a grade be affected?

If a problem is not scored on a scale, the scale should not be counted when assigning the grade.

What if the student doesn't use the content I expected?

When solving problems, students should be encouraged to use any concepts they know. They should not be penalized for approaching the problem in a different way than the teacher expected.

Should I score students' earlier work more easily than later work?

No. The goal is to get students to improve so you should use a consistent scoring throughout the course.

When should I use Level 2, Level 4, and the Star (☆) Level as scores?

Levels 2 and 4 may be used to show performance that falls between the described levels. For example, a student may have used an appropriate approach and found a correct solution to the problem, but then stopped without checking the reasonableness of the solution or trying to verify it. This solution might be scored at Level 4 rather than Level 5. Similarly, a solution that has some of a Level 3 solution might be scored at Level 2. The Star (☆) Level should only be used to indicate exceptional work.

Using Portfolios

Why Portfolios?

Portfolios are a means of assessing students' progress over time. They allow the teacher to focus on a student's collected work rather than on the work of all students on a single activity. Because they provide students with an opportunity for reflection and goal-setting, portfolios are valuable self-assessment tools. By providing tangible evidence of what students have achieved, portfolios help to instill a sense of pride and accomplishment in students and provide very useful tools for communicating with students, parents, and other teachers.

Creating Portfolios

The *Math Thematics* curriculum recognizes the importance of maintaining student portfolios, but understands that there is no single format that will meet the needs of all teachers and all schools using the curriculum. What follows is one possible model.

A portfolio is created cooperatively by the student and the teacher. Work selected for inclusion in the portfolio by the teacher or the student must be accompanied by a *Portfolio Entry Cover Sheet* completed by the student. The cover sheet describes why the piece was chosen, how it reflects the student's understanding of the mathematics content, and any other reflections the student may have. At any time, the student may improve the work. When the student improves a piece, the *Portfolio Entry Cover Sheet* must include what portions were changed and why the student decided to improve the piece.

To create the portfolio, the student should have two folders. In one folder, the student should keep all of the work during a grading period. The student can then look at the work and decide which pieces should be included in the portfolio. The teacher may suggest some pieces to be included. There may also be times when a teacher tells all students to include a particular piece in their portfolios. The student is responsible for organizing the work in the portfolio with suggestions given by the teacher. Some suggestions on what may be included in the portfolio are given on the next page.

Organizing Your Work

Save all your work in the work folder. At any time, you may choose a piece of work to include in your portfolio. All work going into your work folder must be dated and include your name. Keep the following items in your work folder:

- All tests and quizzes.
- All class work and homework assignments.
- All E^2s and *Self-Assessment Forms*.
- *Module Projects*.
- Any other assignment that you needed to complete.

You may improve any piece of work you have completed. When you do, include a written description of what you improved and why you improved the work. This will be helpful if you decide to include the piece in your portfolio.

You may begin creating the actual portfolio at any time by selecting pieces you feel best reflect your work. Each piece must include a *Portfolio Entry Cover Sheet*.

Contents of a Portfolio

Your portfolio represents your work as a mathematics student. It should be something that you would be proud to show other students, teachers, and parents. It must be organized and neat. The portfolio should show the progress you make over a period of time. The following items must be included in your portfolio.

Table of Contents: The first page of your portfolio (not including the cover) should be the *Table of Contents*. The work in your portfolio should be numbered in the same order as in your *Table of Contents*.

Letter to the Reader: The *Letter to the Reader* should give a brief description of how the portfolio reflects your understanding of mathematics and brief descriptions of the pieces in the portfolio.

Self-Assessment Form: The *Self-Assessment Form* gives you the opportunity to reflect on your progress. You may also list any important goals you might have for the next grading period.

Portfolio Entry Cover Sheet: A *Portfolio Entry Cover Sheet* should accompany each piece going into your portfolio.

Work: The work included in your portfolio will vary. Individual pieces may include: *Extended Explorations (E²s)*, *Module Projects*, home or class assignments, tests and quizzes, work from a section, and *Reflecting on the Section* exercises.

Mathematical Autobiography: Your *Mathematical Autobiography* gives you the opportunity to reflect on your past mathematical experiences and attitudes. It should be completed at the beginning of the year.

Attitude Survey: In the *Attitude Survey*, you reflect on your attitudes about mathematics and what improvements could be made in the class.

Portfolio Summary: The *Portfolio Summary* should be included at the end of your portfolio. In it, you should summarize your progress. You also have the opportunity to identify particular goals you may have for the future.

Name _____ Date _____

Portfolio Entry Cover Sheet

I am including this in my portfolio because:

As you review this work, I hope you will notice:

(If this piece needs revision, you must explain how you would improve it and/or what the mistakes were. If you still have difficulties with the mathematics, you need to attach an explanation to this sheet.)

Name _____ Date _____

Self-Assessment Form

For each of the following statements, check the response that best describes your ideas about your work in this grading period.

Problem Solving

	Usually	Sometimes	Rarely
I am able to read the problem successfully and understand what it is about.	☐	☐	☐
I am able to develop a plan and choose a strategy to solve the problem.	☐	☐	☐
I am able to apply problem solving strategies in working through the problem.	☐	☐	☐
I often look back over my work to see that I have answered the questions accurately and completely.	☐	☐	☐

Mathematical Communication

	Usually	Sometimes	Rarely
I use mathematical vocabulary in talking and writing about mathematics.	☐	☐	☐
I feel confident when reading and writing mathematical symbols.	☐	☐	☐
I regularly use and understand models, diagrams, tables, and graphs.	☐	☐	☐

Mathematical Reasoning

	Usually	Sometimes	Rarely
I am able to explain and support my thoughts and conclusions about mathematical ideas.	☐	☐	☐
I am able to understand other people's mathematical thoughts and explanations.	☐	☐	☐

Mathematical Connections

	Usually	Sometimes	Rarely
Remembering what I've already learned helps me understand new math topics.	☐	☐	☐

These are the important things I want to work on:

1.
2.
3.

Math Thematics, Book 2
TR-24 Teacher's Resource Book, Modules 1 and 2

Name _____ Date _____

Mathematical Autobiography

Describe some math experiences that you remember from past school years. Be sure to include your best and worst moments as a mathematics student last year. Also include what expectations you have for yourself this year in math class.

Name _____ Date _____

Portfolio Summary

Write a summary of what you have learned in math class. Be sure to include what you have learned about yourself as a mathematics student and what goals you have for the next grading period.

Name _____ Date _____

Attitude Survey

1. Name two or three of the most important or most interesting things you have learned in math class. Explain why they were interesting or important.

2. Name at least one area of mathematics with which you still need help.

3. How do you feel at this moment about math class? (Circle all that apply. If needed, fill in the blank with another adjective you feel applies.)

interested	successful	excited	happy	relaxed
confused	worried	rushed	frustrated

4. Name one way you can improve math class. Also suggest one way the class as a whole could be improved.

Teacher's Scavenger Hunt

Complete the scavenger hunt below to learn more about the *Math Thematics* program. Use a student textbook, your *Teacher's Edition*, and this *Teacher's Resource Book* to answer these questions.

1. What are the goals of Module 2 Section 3 Exploration 1? Where can you find the goals stated in the student textbook and in the *Teacher's Edition*?

2. The *Math Thematics* program provides a newsletter that can be shared with parents and others as a description of the mathematics to be learned in each module. What is that feature called? Where can you find it for each module?

3. Each section in the student textbook or *Teacher's Edition* begins with a Setting the Stage, which may be a reading passage, an activity, or a visual display. Find an example of each type of Setting the Stage.

4. Materials Lists are provided in the *Teacher's Edition* for each module and section. Give a few examples of materials needed in Module 4.

5. Where can you find a list of all the Technology Resources available in the *Math Thematics* program?

Find a few sections in the student textbook or *Teacher's Edition* that require the use of a Labsheet.

6. If the Labsheet is needed in a Setting the Stage or an Exploration, how was that indicated on the page?

7. How are you and your students told that a Labsheet will be needed in the Practice and Application Exercises?

8. Where would you find a blackline master for Labsheet 4A, which is needed for Module 2 Section 4?

For Questions 9 and 10, look at Module 1 Section 4 in the student textbook and the *Teacher's Edition*.

9. What is the suggested homework assignment after completing Exploration 1? Where in the section are the homework exercises for Exploration 1 identified for the student?

10. Where in the Teacher's Edition is the suggested assignment given for this section?

11. Where can you find additional skill practice, standardized test practice, and study skills support for a section or module?

12. What resources does the *Math Thematics* program provide to help a student who has been absent from class, or to help any student study for a test?

13. Look at the Assessment Scales on either pages 1-6 and 1-7 or pages 2-6 and 2-7 in this *Teacher's Resource Book*. How can these Assessment Scales pages be used by you and your students? (*Hint:* See the information in the *Teacher's Edition*, pages T32–T33, and in this *Teacher's Resource Book*, pages TR-13–TR-21, to help you understand the Assessment Scales.)

14. The student textbook and *Teacher's Edition* include a Review and Assessment for each module. What kind of additional assessments are available to you in the *Teacher's Resource Book* for each module?

15. What pages in the *Teacher's Edition* give a summary of Assessment tools throughout the program?

The student textbook provides an Extended Exploration (E^2) for each module. Questions 16–18 ask you to find materials to accompany these E^2, which appear in other resources.

16. The *Teacher's Edition* gives some background on Managing Extended Explorations. Where is this article located? Where else is information given about the Extended Explorations in this program?

17. Where would you find a possible Solution to the textbook E^2 in Module 2, for example?

18. The program provides an Alternate Extended Exploration (Alternate E^2) for a few modules at each book level. What is the title of the Alternate E^2 for Module 2? Where can it be found?

19. Where is the Scavenger Hunt for your students located? How does it help you and your students understand the student textbook and its resources?

Answers for the Teacher's Scavenger Hunt

1. The goals of Module 2 Section 3 Exploration 1 are "Use tables, graphs, and equations to model sequences." and "Make predictions." The goals are listed in the student textbook next to the start of the Exploration. In the *Teacher's Edition*, goals are given on the module planner and section planner pages at the beginning of each module.

2. The *Teacher's Resource Book*s provide a Math Gazette newsletter for each module that can be sent home to families to explain the math to be learned in that module. For example, in this *Teacher's Resource Book for Modules 1 and 2*, Math Gazettes can be found on pages 1-4–1-5 and pages 2-4–2-5. An article in the *Teacher's Edition* on Communicating with Parents, pages T46–T47, may also be helpful.

3. Sample Responses: Examples of Setting the Stage *reading passages* are Module 1 Section 1, Module 6 Section 1, and Module 8 Section 1. Examples of Setting the Stage *activities* are Module 2 Section 5, Module 4 Section 2, and Module 8 Section 4. Examples of Setting the Stage *visual displays* are Module 2 Section 1, Module 4 Section 1, and Module 5 Section 4.

4. Materials Lists are given at point of use in the student textbook and are provided on module planner and section planner pages before each module in the *Teacher's Edition*. Also, a complete Materials List for Book 2 is given on page TR-31 in this *Teacher's Resource Book for Modules 1 and 2*. Examples of materials needed in Module 4 would be rulers, labsheets, graph paper, and algebra tiles.

5. A list of technology resources is provided on page T35 in the *Teacher's Edition*.

6. The Set Up in a Setting the Stage or Exploration tells what materials are needed, including a list of any labsheets that are needed. (See, for example, Module 1 Section 1 page 3 in the student textbook or *Teacher's Edition*.)

7. In the Practice and Application Exercises, a side note titled "You Will Need" tells you and your students that a labsheet or other materials are required for listed exercises.

8. A labsheet needed for a section in Module 2 would be found in the *Teacher's Resource Book for Modules 1 and 2*. All resources for a particular section are grouped together so look in Section 4 resources. Labsheet 4A is on page 2-38.

9. The homework exercises identified for Module 1 Section 4 Exploration 1 are Exercises 1–24. These are listed for the student at the end of the Exploration on page 48.

10. In the *Teacher's Edition*, a suggested assignment for this section is given on the Section 4 planner page before the module on page 1J and also at point of use at the beginning of the Practice and Application Exercises on page 52. The assignments in the *Teacher's Edition* indicate which exercises to assign on which days of the Exploration. They also provide suggestions for Core Assignments and Extended Assignments.

11. The *Teacher's Resource Books* provide additional Practice and Applications and Study Guide materials with Exercises for each section in a module, and a Standardized Test covering the topics of the whole module.

12. A student who has been absent from class or who is studying for a test can use the Key Concepts pages in the student textbook. The Study Guide materials available for each section in the *Teacher's Resource Books* would also be helpful.

13. The teacher and student can use the Assessment Scales to actively involve the student in assessing his or her own work. As students become more familiar with the scales, they understand what they need to do to improve their problem solving, reasoning, and communication. Teachers assess students' work using the same scales written from a teacher's point of view. The combination of student and teacher assessment provides important feedback to help students improve.

14. For each module, the *Teacher's Resource Book* includes a Module Diagnostic Test, a Mid-Module Quiz, two Module Tests (Forms A and B), a Module Standardized Test, and a Module Performance Assessment. After every two modules, there is a Cumulative Test covering those two modules. The *Teacher's Resource Books* also include a Pre-Course Test before the Module 1 materials, a Mid-Year Test at the end of the Module 4 materials, and an End-of-Year Test at the end of the Module 8 materials.

15. A summary of Assessment tools is provided on pages T30–T31 in the *Teacher's Edition*.

16. In the *Teacher's Edition*, an article on Managing Extended Explorations is given on pages T44–T45. In this *Teacher's Resource Book for Modules 1 and 2* pages 1-39–1-42, more information is provided on the Format for an Extended Exploration, along with Sample Scoring Profiles and Sample Student Solutions.

17. A sample Solution to the textbook E^2 in Module 2 can be found in this *Teacher's Resource Book for Modules 1 and 2* on page 2-26.

18. An Alternate E^2 for Module 2 can be found in this *Teacher's Resource Book for Modules 1 and 2* on pages 2-27–2-28. It is titled "A Calendar Problem."

19. The Scavenger Hunt for the students, located on pages xx–xxi in the student textbook (and on pages T56–T57 in the *Teacher's Edition*), helps students identify all the resources in their textbook modules, in the front of the book, and in the back of the book. It is best used at the beginning of the year so that students will know what is available to them (for example, the Table of Contents, Tables, and Glossary) as they progress through the year.

Literature Connections for *Math Thematics* Book 2

Fiction

- *Hatchet* by Gary Paulsen (Module 1, page 2)

- "Smart" by Shel Silverstein from *Where the Sidewalk Ends* (Module 2, page 124)

- *In Code: A Mathematical Journey* by Sarah Flannery (Module 2, page 130; Module 3, page 201)

- *Zanboomer* by R.R. Knudson (Module 5, page 318)

- *The Horses of Central Park* by Michael Slade (Module 8, page 535)

Historical Fiction and Nonfiction

- "Wed. August 13, 1980" by Eloise Greenfield and Alesia Revis from *Alesia* (Module 2, page 139)

- "There's A Moral Here, Cougar Fans" by Jerry Kirshenbaum from *Sports Illustrated* (Module 2, page 151)

- *Hidden in Plain View* by Jacqueline L. Tobin (Module 3, page 175)

- *Machines* by Robert O'Brien (Module 6, page 392)

- *City in All Directions* by Arnold Adoff (Module 8, page 524)

Materials List for *Math Thematics* Book 2

This is a complete list of materials needed for Book 2 of *Math Thematics*. All quantities are based on a class of 30 students.

Manipulatives

A classroom set of each is needed, unless otherwise noted.

- Pattern blocks
- Number cubes or dice (60 total, 30 red and 60 blue)
- Centimeter cubes
- Algebra tiles
- Cubes (3 different colors)
- Square tiles
- Chips (540)

Regular School Supplies

- Graph paper
- Centimeter grid paper
- Index cards (6 packages, size: 3 in. × 5 in.)
- White paper
- Lined paper
- Yellow paper
- Tracing paper (120 sheets)
- Construction paper (assorted colors)
- Poster board (8 sheets, any color)
- Colored pencils or markers (8 boxes)
- Scissors (15–30)
- Transparent tape

- Masking tape
- Glue bottles or glue sticks (8)
- Compasses (30)
- Protractors (30)
- Rulers (15–30, customary and metric)
- Meter sticks or metric tape (8)
- Yardsticks (8, unless the meter sticks have customary units)
- Customary tape measure (8)
- Watch or clock (with a second hand)
- Paper clips (1 box)
- Push pins or straight pins (8)
- Brass fasteners (1 box)
- Pencils with erasers

Technology

- Calculators (fraction, scientific, and graphing)
- Drawing, spreadsheet, probability, and statistical software (optional)

Additional Supplies

- Uncooked spaghetti (8 pieces)
- Rice (1 large bag)
- Large paper cups (8)
- Colored disks or circular objects (30 or more)
- Pennies (400 total, 8 bags of 50 coins)
- Cotton balls (8)
- Ice cream sticks (150)
- Small cardboard box or eraser (8)
- Mirrors, polyester film, or MIRAs (30)
- "Oddly" shaped containers
- Toothpicks (3 boxes) or drinking straws (750)
- Clipboard or other writing surface
- Rope or heavy string
- Paper bags (30)

Science Supplies

- Balance scale with metric weights (up to 3 kilograms, optional)

PRE-COURSE TEST

NUMBERS AND OPERATIONS ▸▸▸▸▸▸▸▸▸▸▸▸▸▸▸▸▸

Decimals and Whole Numbers (Toolbox, pp. 573–576)

Find each sum or difference. Use mental math when possible.

1. $3.8 + 4.2$ 2. $12.09 + 7.98$ 3. $15.75 - 2.25$ 4. $20.06 - 18.78$

Tell whether each number is divisible by 2, 5, and 10.

5. 504 6. $67,995$ 7. 2550 8. $34,235$

Estimate each sum, difference, product, or quotient.

9. $702 + 895$ 10. $229 - 57$ 11. $8120 \div 92$

12. $589 \cdot 38$ 13. $25.6 - 17.9$ 14. $15.83 + 65.16$

Find each product or quotient.

15. $1.5 \cdot 70$ 16. $3.4 \cdot 25$ 17. $135 \cdot 2.7$

18. $3.78 \div 2$ 19. $17.56 \div 4$ 20. $228.79 \div 10$

Fraction Concepts (Toolbox, pp. 577–580)

Find each value.

21. $\frac{4}{7}$ of 49   22. $\frac{2}{3}$ of 24   23. $\frac{5}{12}$ of 60

Replace each ? with >, <, or =.

24. $\frac{1}{3}$? $\frac{4}{15}$ 25. $\frac{19}{36}$? $\frac{10}{18}$ 26. $\frac{27}{42}$? $\frac{9}{14}$

Find each sum or difference.

27. $\frac{3}{6} + \frac{2}{6}$ 28. $\frac{11}{12} - \frac{4}{12}$ 29. $8\frac{1}{7} + 2\frac{3}{7}$

Modeling Percents and Integers (Toolbox, pp. 581–583)

Sketch a 100-square grid to represent each percent.

30. 26% 31. 83% 32. 12%

Find each sum or difference.

33. $5 + (-14)$ 34. $8 - (-3)$ 35. $-7 - 7$

GEOMETRY AND MEASUREMENT ▸▸▸▸▸▸▸▸▸▸▸▸▸▸▸▸▸

Using and Converting Measurements (Toolbox, pp. 584–585)

Find the perimeter of each figure.

36.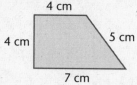

37.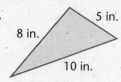

Replace each ? with the correct number. Use the Table of Measures on page 590.

38. 48 oz = __?__ lb   39. 5 ft = __?__ in.   40. 10,560 ft = __?__ mi   41. 18 yd = __?__ in.

Perimeter and Area of a Rectangle (Toolbox, p. 586)

Find the perimeter and the area of each rectangle.

42. a rectangle with length 9 in. and width 2 in.

43. a rectangle with length 7 m and width 5 m

DATA ANALYSIS AND DISPLAYS ▸▸▸▸▸▸▸▸▸▸▸▸▸▸▸▸▸

Making Bar Graphs and Line Graphs (Toolbox, pp. 587–588)

44. Make a bar graph of the data below.

Day	Mon	Tues	Wed	Thurs	Fri
Minutes of exercise	30	50	45	20	30

45. Make a line graph of the data below.

Minutes of exercise	0	5	10	15
Heart rate (beats per minute)	72	90	124	130

Finding the Mean (Toolbox, p. 588)

Find the mean of the data.

46. 20, 24, 43, 32, 35, 16, 18, 36

47. 250, 175, 205, 270, 300, 180

Contents

Book 2	Teacher's Resources for Module 1

Search and Rescue

Name _____   Date _____

Module Diagnostic Test
For use before Module 1

1. Use a protractor to draw an angle that measures 115°. Then classify the angle as *acute*, *obtuse*, *right*, or *straight*.   (Sec. 1)

2. Use the diagram at the right. Which of the following angles   (Sec. 1)

   A. ∠*COM*   **B.** ∠*COP*   **C.** ∠*MOP*   **D.** ∠*POD*

   is supplementary to ∠*COD*? _____

   is complementary to ∠*COD*? _____

   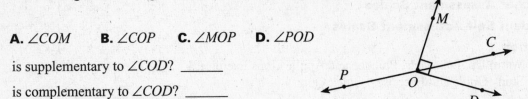

3. Evaluate the following expression using the order of operations.   (Sec. 1)

   $3 + 2 \cdot 4 + 8$

   A. 28   **B.** 60   **C.** 19

4. Which list shows the integers in order from least to greatest?   (Sec. 2)

   A. −11, −5, 0, 4, 19   **B.** −5, −11, 0, 4, 19   **C.** 0, 4, −5, −11, 19

5. Compare $|-8|$ and $|8|$ using <, >, or =.   (Sec. 2)

   A. $|-8| < |8|$ **B.** $|-8| > |8|$ **C.** $|-8| = |8|$

6. Which of the following are the coordinates of point *B*?   (Sec. 2)

   A. (−4, 3)
   B. (−4, −3)
   C. (4, −3)
   D. (−3, 4)
   E. (−3, −4)

7. Which of the following illustrates the commutative property of addition?   (Sec. 3)

   A. $(13 + 10) + 2 = 12 + (11 + 2)$ **B.** $5 + 3 = 8 + 0$

   C. $7 + (4 + 2) = 7 + 6$ **D.** $5 + 9 = 9 + 5$

Module Diagnostic Test
For use before Module 1

8. Which of the following illustrates the associative property of addition? (Sec. 3)

   A. $10 + 2 = 12 + 0$ **B.** $6 + (5 + 2) = 6 + (2 + 5)$

   C. $7 + (4 + 2) = (7 + 4) + 2$ **D.** $3 + 20 = 20 + 3$

9. Evaluate the following expression. (Sec. 3)

   $-5 - 15$

   A. -20 **B.** -10 **C.** 10 **D.** 20

Evaluate each expression when $m = 4$, $b = -2$, and $n = -3$. (Sec. 4)

10. $3m + b + n$ 11. $m - n$

12. Complete the table of values for the equation $y = 2x - 5$. Then graph the equation. (Sec. 4)

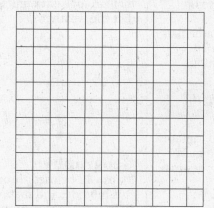

x	y
1	
2	
3	
4	
5	

Show how to use inverse operations to solve each equation. (Sec. 5)

13. $34 = 19 + x$ 14. $\frac{w}{6} = 132$ 15. $k - 9 = -87$

16. Adam's December electric bill was 3 times the cost of his bill in August. Write an (Sec. 5)
equation using two variables to describe the relationship between Adam's August
and December electric bills. Identify the variables you use.

The Math Gazette
Search and Rescue

Sneak Preview!

Over the next several weeks in our mathematics class, we will be developing geometry, measurement, coordinate graphing, and pre-algebra concepts while completing a thematic unit on Search and Rescue. Some of the topics we will be discussing are:

▶ the techniques and skills necessary for planning a search

▶ weather and geographic conditions

▶ preparation for searches—clothing, food, and so on

We will look at how mathematics can be used in a variety of search and rescue situations.

Ask Your Student

How do pilots and ship captains navigate their vessels to make certain they reach their destinations? (Sec. 1)

In what ways is mathematics used to describe the weather? (Sec. 2 and Sec. 3)

Why is a balance scale a good model for an equation? (Sec. 5)

Connections

Literature:
Students will read excerpts from *Hatchet*, by Gary Paulsen. In the story, a boy is forced to fly a plane after the pilot has a heart attack. You may enjoy reading this novel together.

Science:
Students will read about extreme weather conditions encountered by missing people and searchers. Discuss with your student how weather affects your daily lives. Your student may also be interested in how a meteorologist attempts to predict the weather.

Geography:
Maps will be used throughout this module, and map reading skills, such as determining headings, using scale, and locating points with coordinates, will be discussed. Look for different types of maps in newspapers, magazines, or around the house and discuss them with your student. How are they read? What do they show? What is the scale?

E² Project

Following Section 3, students will have approximately one week to complete the Extended Exploration (E²), *A Phone Chain*. Students will use drawings, diagrams, or tables to determine how long it may take for members of a search and rescue team to be notified of a missing plane or person by way of a phone chain.

Students might need the following material for the project:

▶ large sheets of blank paper for drawing diagrams

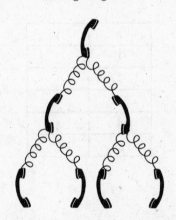

Module Project

After completing the module, students will imagine that they are members of a search and rescue team and develop a search strategy for finding a lost person. They will write a newspaper article about planning their search.

Search and Rescue

Section Title	Mathematics Students Will Be Learning	Activities
1: Heading Out	◆ naming, measuring, drawing, and classifying angles ◆ identifying supplementary and complementary angles and finding their measures ◆ using order of operations	◆ use a protractor and magnetic compass to measure angles and determine headings ◆ use a map to devise a search plan for a missing plane
2: Searching for Integers	◆ comparing integers ◆ finding opposites and absolute values of integers ◆ identifying and plotting points on a coordinate plane ◆ identifying parallel and perpendicular lines on a plane	◆ read charts and contour maps
3: A Call for Help	◆ adding and subtracting integers ◆ using properties of addition	◆ add and subtract integers by "hiking" on a number line ◆ explore wind-chill temperatures
4: Urban Rescue	◆ modeling functions with tables, equations, and graphs ◆ evaluating expressions containing variables	◆ use equations to determine how long it takes to transport an injured person to a hospital ◆ use graphing to compare functions and solve a system of linear equations
5: Searching for a Solution	◆ writing equations to model situations ◆ solving one-step equations	◆ model equations using a balance scale ◆ model and solve equations using algebra tiles and inverse operations

Activities to do at Home

◆ Plan a dream vacation across the United States. Choose several places you would like to visit and use a map to estimate the headings a plane would have to follow and the distances if you traveled by airplane. (After Sec. 1)

◆ Does the weather seem unusually hot or cold this year? Track the high and low temperatures reported in your newspaper for several weeks. Make a chart to compare the temperatures in your town or city to several other places in the country or world. (After Sec. 2)

◆ Look for articles in newspapers or magazines about search and rescue missions. Discuss the conditions and adversities faced by the missing people and the searchers. (After Sec. 3)

Related Topics

You may want to discuss these related topics with your student:

 Navigation and orienteering

 Meteorology

 Cartography

 Camping and survival in the wilderness

Name _____   Problem _____

Teacher Assessment Scales

For use with Module 1

☆ *The star indicates that you excelled in some way.*

 ## Problem Solving

1   **2**   **3**   **4**   **5**   ☆→

You did not understand the problem well enough to get started or you did not show any work.

You understood the problem well enough to make a plan and to work toward a solution.

You made a plan, you used it to solve the problem, and you verified your solution.

 ## Mathematical Language

1   **2**   **3**   **4**   **5**   ☆→

You did not use any mathematical vocabulary or symbols, or you did not use them correctly, or your use was not appropriate.

You used appropriate mathematical language, but the way it was used was not always correct or other terms and symbols were needed.

You used mathematical language that was correct and appropriate to make your meaning clear.

 ## Representations

1   **2**   **3**   **4**   **5**   ☆→

You did not use any representations such as equations, tables, graphs, or diagrams to help solve the problem or explain your solution.

You made appropriate representations to help solve the problem or help you explain your solution, but they were not always correct or other representations were needed.

You used appropriate and correct representations to solve the problem or explain your solution.

 ## Connections

1   **2**   **3**   **4**   **5**   ☆→

You attempted or solved the problem and then stopped.

You found patterns and used them to extend the solution to other cases, or you recognized that this problem relates to other problems, mathematical ideas, or applications.

You extended the ideas in the solution to the general case, or you showed how this problem relates to other problems, mathematical ideas, or applications.

 ## Presentation

1   **2**   **3**   **4**   **5**   ☆→

The presentation of your solution and reasoning is unclear to others.

The presentation of your solution and reasoning is clear in most places, but others may have trouble understanding parts of it.

The presentation of your solution and reasoning is clear and can be understood by others.

Content Used: _____   **Computational Errors:**   Yes ☐ No ☐

Notes on Errors: _____

_____

Math Thematics, Book 2
Teacher's Resource Book, Modules 1 and 2

MODULE 1

Student Self-Assessment Scales

For use with Module 1

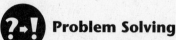 If your score is in the shaded area, explain why on the back of this sheet and stop.

☆ The star indicates that you excelled in some way.

 ## Problem Solving

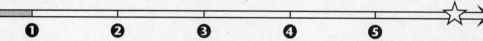

❶   **❷**   **❸**   **❹**   **❺**

I did not understand the problem well enough to get started or I did not show any work.

I understood the problem well enough to make a plan and to work toward a solution.

I made a plan, I used it to solve the problem, and I verified my solution.

 ## Mathematical Language

❶   **❷**   **❸**   **❹**   **❺**

I did not use any mathematical vocabulary or symbols, or I did not use them correctly, or my use was not appropriate.

I used appropriate mathematical language, but the way it was used was not always correct or other terms and symbols were needed.

I used mathematical language that was correct and appropriate to make my meaning clear.

Representations

❶   **❷**   **❸**   **❹**   **❺**

I did not use any representations such as equations, tables, graphs, or diagrams to help solve the problem or explain my solution.

I made appropriate representations to help solve the problem or help me explain my solution, but they were not always correct or other representations were needed.

I used appropriate and correct representations to solve the problem or explain my solution.

 ## Connections

❶   **❷**   **❸**   **❹**   **❺**

I attempted or solved the problem and then stopped.

I found patterns and used them to extend the solution to other cases, or I recognized that this problem relates to other problems, mathematical ideas, or applications.

I extended the ideas in the solution to the general case, or I showed how this problem relates to other problems, mathematical ideas, or applications.

 ## Presentation

❶   **❷**   **❸**   **❹**   **❺**

The presentation of my solution and reasoning is unclear to others.

The presentation of my solution and reasoning is clear in most places, but others may have trouble understanding parts of it.

The presentation of my solution and reasoning is clear and can be understood by others.

Name _____   Date _____

Warm-Up Exercises

For use with Section 1

Illustrate each term with a drawing and state its dimension.

1. point

2. line

3. plane

4. cube

ANSWERS

1. •; no dimension   2. ⟷ ; 1 dimension

3. ▱ ; 2 dimensions   4. ⬡ ; 3 dimensions

Name _____ Date _____

Types of Angles (Use with Question 8 on page 5.)

Directions

- First, estimate the measure of each angle.
- Then, use a protractor to measure each angle.

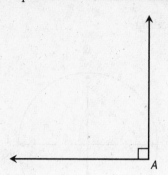

a. Estimated measure _____

    Actual measure _____

      a *right* angle

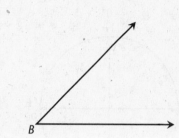

b. Estimated measure _____

    Actual measure _____

      an *acute* angle

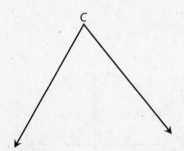

c. Estimated measure _____

    Actual measure _____

      an *acute* angle

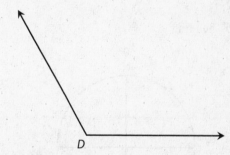

d. Estimated measure _____

    Actual measure _____

      an *obtuse* angle

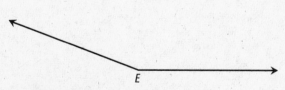

e. Estimated measure _____

    Actual measure _____

      an *obtuse* angle

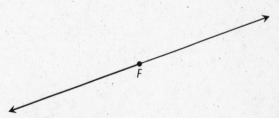

f. Estimated measure _____

    Actual measure _____

      a *straight* angle

MODULE 1   **LABSHEET** **1B**

Heading Diagrams (Use with Question 11 on page 6 and Question 18 on page 8.)

Directions Without using a protractor, estimate each heading and draw a ray to represent it.

a. 20° heading

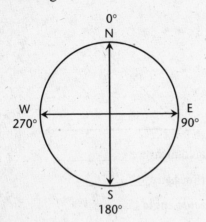

b. 120° heading

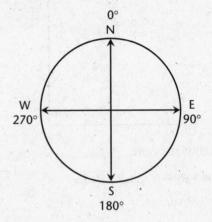

c. 225° heading

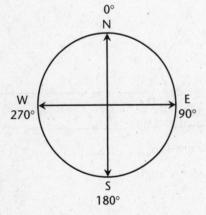

d. 345° heading

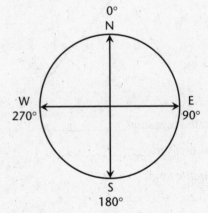

Math Thematics, Book 2
Teacher's Resource Book, Modules 1 and 2

Name _____ Date _____

Plotting a Heading (Use with Question 19 on page 8.)

Directions In the reading from *Hatchet* in your textbook, Brian guesses that
the 342 on the display might be a compass heading. Suppose Brian's plane is at
the center of the compass diagram on the map below.

a. Estimate a heading of 342° by drawing a dashed ray on the compass diagram.

b. Use a protractor to measure a heading of 342°. Use a solid ray to plot the
heading. How do the two rays compare?

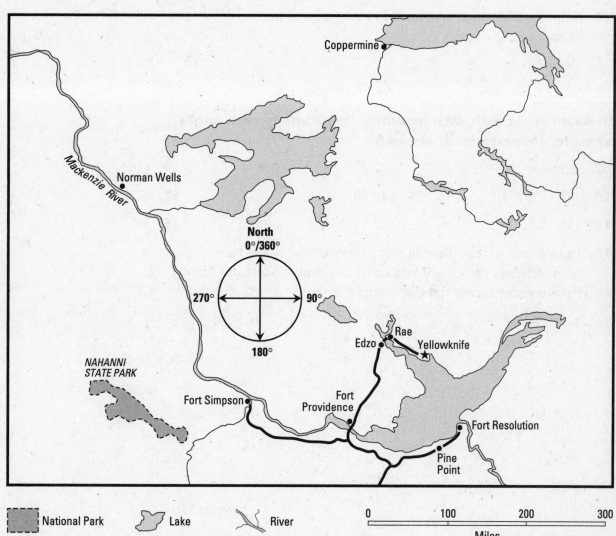

Name _____   Date _____

For use with Exploration 1

For Exercises 1–6, use the diagram.

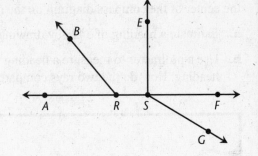

1. Name three angles that have point *R* as a vertex.

2. Name all the angles that have $\overrightarrow{SA}$ as a side.

3. Name two straight angles.

4. Name an acute angle that has *S* as its vertex and find its measure.

5. Name a right angle.

6. Name three obtuse angles and find their measures.

Draw an angle with each measure. Then classify each angle as *acute, obtuse, right,* or *straight*.

7. 155°	**8.** 25°	**9.** 180°
10. 90°	**11.** 38°	**12.** 97°
13. 15°	**14.** 170°	**15.** 56°

16. Draw hands to show the following times on the clocks below. Name whether each angle formed by the minute hand and hour hand is *acute, obtuse, right,* or *straight*.

a. 3:00   **b.** 7:30

c. 6:00   **d.** 5:00

(continued)

Practice and Applications

For use with Section 1

For use with Exploration 2

17. Plane 1 is flying from point *A* at a heading of 50°. Plane 2 is flying from point *A* at a heading of 140°. What is the measure of the angle formed by the flight paths of the two planes?

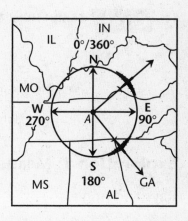

For each angle measure:

a. Find the measure of a supplementary angle.

b. Find the measure of a complementary angle, if possible.

18. 25°   **19.** 172°   **20.** 72°   **21.** 90°

22. 43°   **23.** 20°   **24.** 146°   **25.** 108°

For Exercises 26 and 27, refer to the map at the right.

26. A private plane and a jumbo jet both leave from Cary, but in opposite directions. The private plane is flying toward Jasper at a heading of 223°. What is the heading for the jumbo jet?

27. Morris is located due north of Jasper. Measure on the map with a protractor to find what heading should be used for a flight from Morris to Cary.

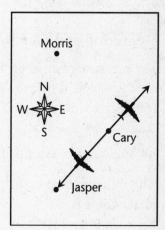

For use with Exploration 3

28. Evaluate each expression using the order of operations.

    a. $36 - 4 \cdot 5$ **b.** $8 \cdot (3 + 7) - 5$ **c.** $15 + 18 \div 3^2 - 6$

    d. $(8 - 3)^2 \cdot (14 - 8)$ **e.** $\dfrac{80 \div (6 - 2)}{35 \div 7}$ **f.** $2^4 \div [5^2 - (13 + 7)]$

29. Write and evaluate an expression to represent the value in cents of 3 half dollars, 3 quarters, 8 nickels, 4 dimes, and 2 pennies.

30. Use grouping symbols to make each statement true.

    a. $25 - 8 \cdot 3 = 51$ **b.** $9 + 9 \div 3 \cdot 5 - 3 = 12$ **c.** $6 \cdot 5 - 5^2 + 2 = 3$

Name _____ Date _____

Study Guide
For use with Section 1

Heading Out   Angles and Order of Operations

GOAL   **LEARN HOW TO:** • draw, name, measure, and classify angles
• use supplementary angles and complementary angles
• use exponents
• evaluate expressions using the order of operations

AS YOU: • learn a skill SAR team members need
• find compass headings
• solve problems

Exploration 1: Measuring Angles

Rays and Angles

A **ray** is a part of a line. It starts at an endpoint and goes on forever in
one direction. Ray *BC* is written $\overrightarrow{BC}$. Always write the endpoint first.

An **angle** is formed by two rays with a common endpoint. The rays
are the angle's **sides**, and the endpoint is called the **vertex** of the angle.
The angle at the right, formed by $\overrightarrow{BA}$ and $\overrightarrow{BC}$, can be called ∠ABC, ∠CBA,
or ∠B. Always write the vertex as the middle letter.

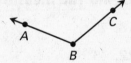

Measuring and Classifying Angles

The measure of an angle is the amount of rotation between its two
rays. An angle is measured in units called **degrees**. There are
180 degrees in a straight line.

An angle can be classified by its measure.

| The measure of an **acute angle** is between 0° and 90°. | The measure of a **right angle** is exactly 90°. | The measure of an **obtuse angle** is between 90° and 180°. | The measure of a **straight angle** is exactly 180°. |

$m\angle Q = 50°$ $\qquad$ $m\angle R = 90°$ $\qquad$ $m\angle S = 105°$ $\qquad$ $m\angle T = 180°$

Name _____   Date _____

Study Guide
For use with Section 1

Exploration 2: Angle Relationships

Supplementary and Complementary

Two angles are **supplementary angles** if the sum of the measures of the angles is 180°. ∠P and ∠Q at the right are supplementary angles.

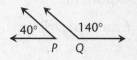

Two angles are **complementary angles** if the sum of the measures of the angles is 90°. ∠X and ∠Y at the right are complementary angles.

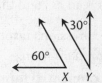

Example

Refer to the diagram.

a. Name two angles that are complementary.

b. Name two angles that are supplementary.

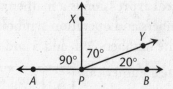

■ Sample Response ■

a. To identify two complementary angles, look for a *sum* of 90°.

Since $m\angle XPY = 70°$ and $m\angle YPB = 20°$, and 70° + 20° = 90°, ∠XPY and ∠YPB are complementary angles.

b. To identify two supplementary angles, look for a *sum* of 180° or look for two angles that form a straight angle.

∠APB is a straight angle. One pair of angles that forms ∠APB is ∠APY and ∠YPB.

Notice that $m\angle APY = 90° + 70°$, or 160°, $m\angle YPB = 20°$, and 160° + 20° = 180°.

So, ∠APY and ∠YPB are one pair of supplementary angles.

Two other angles that are supplementary are ∠APX and ∠BPX, whose measures are 90° and 70° + 20°, or 90°, respectively.

Name _____   Date _____

 **Study Guide**
For use with Section 1

Exploration 3: Order of Operations

Exponents

Exponents tell you how many times a **base** is used as a factor. In the expression 6^3, "6" is the base and "3" is the exponent. The expression 6^3 is read as "6 to the 3rd **power**." 6^3 is equal to $6 \cdot 6 \cdot 6$.

Expressions involving exponents can be written in *exponential form* or *standard form*.

exponential form $\rightarrow$ 6^3 **standard form** $\rightarrow$ 216

Order of Operations

A **numerical expression** is a mathematical phrase that can be formed using numbers and operation symbols. The expression $3 \cdot 4 + 5$ contains the numbers 3, 4, and 5 and the operation symbols $\cdot$ and $+$.

To **evaluate** a numerical expression, you carry out the mathematical operations in the correct order, known as the **order of operations**. The mnemonic Please Excuse My Dear Aunt Sally (**PEMDAS**) can help you remember the order of operations.

P	First carry out operations within *parentheses* or other **grouping symbols**, such as brackets or fraction bars.
E	Next evaluate expressions involving *exponents*.
M	Then, perform *multiplication* . . .
D	. . . and *division*, moving from left to right.
A	Finally, perform *addition* . . .
S	. . . and *subtraction*, again moving from left to right.

Example

Evaluate the expression $2 + [2 \cdot (8 - 3)^2 \div 5] \div 2$ using the order of operations.

Sample Response

$2 + [2 \cdot (\mathbf{8 - 3})^2 \div 5] \div 2$	$\leftarrow$ Evaluate within parentheses.
$2 + [2 \cdot \mathbf{5^2} \div 5] \div 2$	$\leftarrow$ Evaluate expressions involving exponents.
$2 + [\mathbf{2 \cdot 25} \div 5] \div 2$	$\leftarrow$ Within the brackets, multiply and divide, moving from left to right.
$2 + [\mathbf{50 \div 5}] \div 2$	
$2 + \mathbf{10 \div 2}$	$\leftarrow$ Divide.
$\mathbf{2 + 5}$	$\leftarrow$ Add.
7	

Math Thematics, Book 2
Teacher's Resource Book, Modules 1 and 2

Name _____ Date _____

Study Guide: Practice & Application Exercises

For use with Section 1

Exploration 1

For Exercises 1–5, use the diagram.

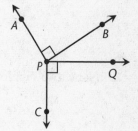

1. Name the ray that passes through point Q.

2. Name an acute angle and find its measure.

3. Name three angles that have $\overrightarrow{PB}$ as a side.

4. **Visual Thinking** Name all the angles that have vertex P.

5. Name two obtuse angles that have the same measure. What is the measure of these angles?

Exploration 2

For Exercises 6–8, use the diagram.

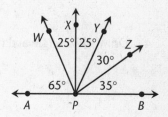

6. Name four pairs of supplementary angles.

7. Name five pairs of complementary angles.

8. **Writing** Are $\angle XPY$, $\angle YPZ$, and $\angle ZPB$ complementary angles? Explain.

9. Draw a pair of supplementary angles that are of equal measure. Classify these angles.

10. **Challenge** Find the measure of the angle whose complementary angle measures $\frac{1}{3}$ of its supplementary angle.

Exploration 3

For Exercises 11–21, evaluate each expression using the order of operations.

11. $36 - 5 \cdot 6$

12. $8 \cdot (5 + 7) - 4$

13. $4 \cdot 3 - 8 \div 2$

14. $10 + 25 \div 5 + 3^2$

15. $48 \div (13 - 7) \cdot 4$

16. $(12 - 9)^2 - (12 - 9)$

17. $\dfrac{(15 + 1) \cdot 2}{6 + 2}$

18. $\dfrac{90 \div (10 \div 5)}{9 - 4}$

19. $2^3 \div [3^2 - (5 + 3)]$

20. Write and evaluate an expression to represent the value in cents of 3 dollars, 2 half-dollars, 7 dimes, 4 nickels, and 8 pennies.

21. **Challenge** Use grouping symbols to make the statement $2^3 + 6^2 - 4^2 \div 4 - 2 \cdot 3 = 7$ true.

Name _____   Date _____

1. Name two acute angles in the figure at the right.

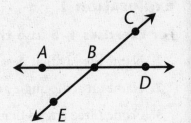

2. Name two supplementary angles in the figure at the right.

3. What is the measure of an angle complementary to 40°?
   What is the measure of an angle supplementary to 40°?

4. Draw a 40° angle and the two other angles you described in Question 3.

5. Measure the heading.

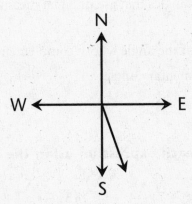

6. Write $11 \cdot 11 \cdot 11 \cdot 11$ in exponential form.

7. Use the order of operations to evaluate $14 + 10 \cdot 2^2 - (16 \div 8)$.

Name _____   Date _____

Warm-Up Exercises

For use with Section 2

Compare the two given numbers. Use <, >, or =.

1. 21 _____ 12

2. 8 _____ 6

3. 6 _____ 8

4. 4.00 _____ 4

5. 0.09 _____ 0.0900

6. 0 _____ 0.1

ANSWERS

1. >   2. >   3. <   4. =   5. =   6. <

Name _____   Date _____

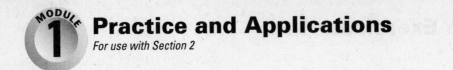

Practice and Applications
For use with Section 2

For use with Exploration 1

1. Write each quantity using symbols instead of words.

   a. New Orleans, Louisiana is 8 ft below sea level.

   b. Big Stone Lake in South Dakota is 966 ft above sea level.

   c. For the first big drop on a roller coaster ride, the speed of Kim's car increased 60 miles per hour.

   d. Maurice lost 480 points on a quiz show.

2. Refer to the number line.

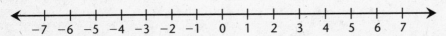

   a. Where on the number line are the integers less than –2?

   b. List all the negative integers that are greater than –4.

   c. List all the positive integers that are less than 6.

   d. List all the integers that are less than 3 but greater than –7.

3. Replace each ___?___ with > or <.

   a. –8 ___?___ –5   **b.** 0 ___?___ –2   **c.** –9 ___?___ 9

   d. 12 ___?___ 7   **e.** –13 ___?___ –17   **f.** –25 ___?___ 14

4. Find the opposite of each integer.

   a. –12   **b.** 53   **c.** –42

   d. 26   **e.** 0   **f.** –84

5. Find each absolute value.

   a. |–8| **b.** |23| **c.** |–95|

   d. |95| **e.** |–16| **f.** |44|

6. Replace each ___?___ with > or <.

   a. 6 ___?___ |–15| **b.** –8 ___?___ |–8| **c.** |–21| ___?___ |–3|

(continued)

Math Thematics, Book 2
Teacher's Resource Book, Modules 1 and 2

Name _____   Date _____

Practice and Applications

For use with Section 2

For use with Exploration 2

For Exercises 7–11, refer to the coordinate plane shown below.

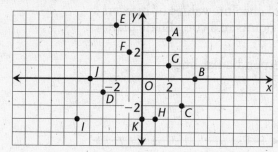

7. **a.** Name a point on the horizontal *x*-axis.

   b. Name a point on the vertical *y*-axis.

   c. Is the line through *A* and *G* horizontal or vertical?

   d. Is the line through *H* and *I* horizontal or vertical?

   e. How many horizontal lines go through point *D*?

   f. How many vertical lines go through point *D*?

8. Write the coordinates of each point.

   a. *C*   **b.** *E*   **c.** *A*

   d. *I*   **e.** *J*   **f.** *K*

9. Name two points that have the same first coordinate.

10. Name three points that have the same second coordinate.

11. Plot each point in a coordinate plane. Use the grid shown above.

   a. $M(6, -3)$ **b.** $N(-7, 0)$ **c.** $P(-8, 4)$

   d. $Q(7, 2)$ **e.** $R(-8, -4)$ **f.** $S(0, 1)$

12. How can you draw axes on a flat, rectangular table top so that the points on the table top can be located without using any negative coordinates? Can you do this for a mathematical plane? Explain your thinking.

Name _____   Date _____

Study Guide
For use with Section 2

Searching for Integers   Integers and Coordinates

GOAL   **LEARN HOW TO:** • compare integers
• find opposites and absolute values of integers
• identify and plot points in a coordinate plane

AS YOU: • learn about elevation
• work with parallel and perpendicular lines

Exploration 1: Comparing Integers

Integers

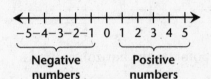

Numbers greater than zero are **positive**.

Numbers less than zero are **negative**.

Integers are the counting numbers, their opposites, and zero. Two numbers are **opposites** if they are the same distance from 0 on a number line but on opposite sides of 0.

The opposite of 5 is −5.
The opposite of −8 is 8.
The opposite of 0 is 0.

The integers are the numbers …, −4, −3, −2, −1, 0, 1, 2, 3, 4, … .

An **inequality** is a mathematical sentence stating that one quantity is greater than or less than another. You can write inequalities to compare integers.

−3 is greater than −6   or   −6 is less than −3
        −3 > −6   −6 < −3

Example

Write two inequalities to compare −9 and 7.

Sample Response

Graph the numbers on a number line. The integers increase as you go from left to right.

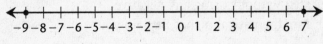

−9 < 7 or 7 > −9

Study Guide
For use with Section 2

The **absolute value** of a number is the distance from the number to 0 on a number line. You read |–3| as "the absolute value of negative three."

Example
Find the absolute value of –5 and 5.

■ Sample Response ■

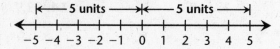

–5 is 5 units from 0, so |–5| = 5.

5 is 5 units from 0, so |5| = 5.

Exploration 2: Coordinate Graphing

Line Relationships

A **plane** can be thought of as a flat surface that goes on forever.

Two lines **intersect** if they meet or cross each other. Lines *a* and *b* intersect.

Two lines in a plane are **parallel** if they do not intersect. Lines *c* and *d* are parallel.

Two lines are **perpendicular** if they intersect at 90° angles. Lines *e* and *f* are perpendicular.

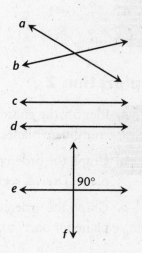

Graphing in a Coordinate Plane

The **coordinate plane** is a grid with a **horizontal *x*-axis** and a **vertical *y*-axis** that intersect at the **origin**.

An **ordered pair** of numbers, called **coordinates,** can be used to identify and plot points in a coordinate plane.

The *first coordinate* in an ordered pair gives a point's location to the left or right of zero on the horizontal axis. The *second coordinate* gives the point's location up or down from zero on the vertical axis.

The ordered pair for the origin is (0, 0).

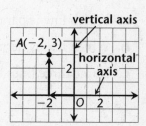

Point *A* has coordinates (–2, 3).

(–2, 3)

2 units left   3 units up

Name _____ Date _____

Study Guide: Practice & Application Exercises
For use with Section 2

Exploration 1

Replace each __?__ with > or <.

1. 9 __?__ 5

2. 0 __?__ –5

3. 43 __?__ –53

4. –16 __?__ –20

5. –3 __?__ –1

6. 8 __?__ 11

Find the opposite of each integer.

7. 5

8. –30

9. 588

10. –19

11. –333

12. –8

13. 103

14. 22,973

Find the absolute value of each integer.

15. $|{-10}|$

16. $|50|$

17. $|{-2}|$

18. $|312|$

19. $|{-6}|$

20. $|31|$

21. $|105|$

22. $|{-776}|$

Replace each __?__ with > or <.

23. 41 __?__ –41

24. $|{-3}|$ __?__ $|{-7}|$

25. –4 __?__ –5

26. –6 __?__ 13

27. $|2|$ __?__ $|{-8}|$

28. $|{-12}|$ __?__ $|10|$

Exploration 2

29. **a.** Identify the coordinates of the points *A* through *E* in the coordinate plane.

   b. Graph the ordered pairs (–3, 5) and (–3, –3) in a coordinate plane. Draw a segment to connect the points.

   c. Graph the ordered pairs (–1, 4) and (–4, 1) in the coordinate plane for part (b). Draw a segment to connect the points.

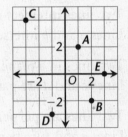

30. Use the diagram at the right for Exercise 30.

   a. Which line is parallel to line *a*?

   b. Which line is perpendicular to line *b*?

   c. Name three lines that line *c* intersects.

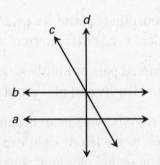

Math Thematics, Book 2
Teacher's Resource Book, Modules 1 and 2

Name _____   Date _____

Quick Quiz
For use after Section 2

1. Represent this temperature change using an integer and an appropriate unit of measure: *The temperature dropped 29°F.*

2. Find the next three terms in the sequence 14, 8, 2, ...

3. What is the opposite of 18,942?

4. Is |−11| greater than or less than 10?

5. Graph (−2, −4), (3, −1), and (−5, 2) in a coordinate plane.

Name _____   Date _____

Warm-Up Exercises
For use with Section 3

Use mental math to add or subtract.

1. $14 + 9$

2. $5 + 15 + 10$

3. $8 + 3 + 17$

4. $16 - 4$

5. $27 - 16$

6. $38 - 19$

ANSWERS

1. 23   2. 30   3. 28   4. 12   5. 11   6. 19

Name _____   Date _____

Number Line Markers (Use with Question 3 on page 30.)

Directions

- Cut out these number line markers.

- Arrange the markers on the floor from least to greatest to create a number line. Place them about 1 ft apart.

- Place the direction labels at the appropriate ends of the number line.

−6	−5	−4	−3
−2	−1	0	1
2	3	4	5
6	POSITIVE DIRECTION		
	NEGATIVE DIRECTION		

Spinner for Hiking (Use with Question 3 on page 30.)

Directions

• Cut out each spinner along the rectangular border.

• Unfold three paper clips to use as pointers for the spinners.

• When you spin the pointer, hold it in place with the tip of a pen or pencil at the center of the spinner.

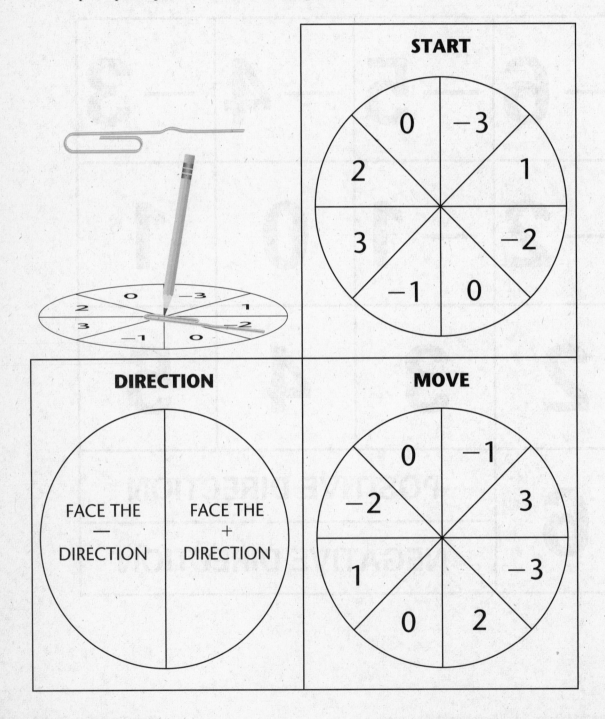

Name _____ Date _____

Table of Hikes (Use with Question 4 on page 31 and Question 6 on page 32.)

Directions Take turns hiking on your number line as described on page 30. Record each hike and the finishing position in the table. Continue until the table is full.

Hiker's name	Started at	Direction faced	Moved		Finishing position
Example	**2** The starting position of the hike is 2.	**–** – tells the hiker to face the negative direction.	**–3** –3 tells the hiker to move backward 3 units.	**=**	**5**
				=	
				=	
				=	
				=	
				=	
				=	
				=	
				=	
				=	
				=	
				=	
				=	

Name _____ Date _____

Adding Two Integers with Opposite Signs (Use with Question 18 on page 33.)

Directions Complete the table and questions below by thinking about each integer's position on a number line. The first row of the table is filled in as an example.

Integer 1 + Integer 2	Distance from zero (absolute value)		How much farther on a number line is one of the integers from zero than the other?	Will the sum be + or –?	Addition sentence and sum
	Integer 1	Integer 2			
7 + (–9)	7	9	2	–	7 + (–9) = –2
–3 + 14					
–20 + 21					
21 + (–20)					
15 + (–10)					
–36 + 23					

a. Explain how you could use absolute values to add any two integers with different signs.

b. Use the method you described in part (a) to add –18 + 24.

c. Use a number line to check your answer to part (b).

Name _____ Date _____

Practice and Applications
For use with Section 3

For use with Exploration 1

A hiker on a number line follows each set of directions. Determine where the hiker will finish. Record the moves as an addition problem with its sum or as a subtraction problem with its difference.

1. Start at –6. Face the negative direction. Move backward 2 units.

2. Start at 4. Face the positive direction. Move backward 6 units.

3. Start at 3. Face the negative direction. Move forward 7 units.

4. Start at –3. Face the positive direction. Move forward 5 units.

For use with Exploration 2

Use a number line to find each sum. Then write the addition problem with its sum.

5. $-4 + 8$

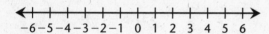

6. $3 + (-5)$

7. $-2 + (-3)$

8. $0 + (-2)$

Find each sum.

9. $3 + (-9)$

10. $-7 + 2$

11. $-5 + (-4)$

12. $-8 + 8$

13. $12 + (-6)$

14. $-11 + 7$

15. $16 + (-10)$

16. $-9 + (-5)$

17. $-13 + 4$

For Exercises 18–20, write and evaluate an addition expression to model each situation.

18. The temperature at 2 P.M. was –3°F. By 5 P.M., the temperature had risen 12°F.

19. In the first round of a game, Gabriela lost 500 points. In the second round, she gained 900 points.

20. A weather balloon was released from the top of a hill 250 ft above sea level. The balloon rose 830 ft and was later found floating in the ocean a few miles away.

(continued)

MODULE 1 Practice and Applications
For use with Section 3

For use with Exploration 3

Use a number line to find each difference. Then write the subtraction problem with its difference.

21. −1 − (−6)

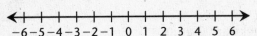

22. 5 − 8

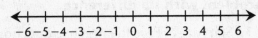

23. −3 − 3

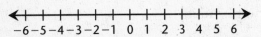

24. 2 − (−4)

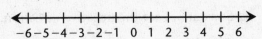

Rewrite each subtraction problem as the related addition problem that has the same answer.

25. −17 − 2

26. 8 − (−4)

27. 5 − 10

28. −15 − (−6)

29. 30 − 42

30. −9 − (−25)

Find each difference.

31. 7 − 11

32. −3 − 8

33. 5 − (−4)

34. −20 − (−10)

35. −35 − 16

36. −29 − (−15)

Evaluate each expression.

37. 3 + (−7) −12

38. −42 + 6 − 15

39. (8 − 14) − (−3)

40. −2 − (4 − 29)

41. (8 − 3) − (3 − 8)

42. −6 + (−9) − (−2)

43. The greatest known depth in the Pacific Ocean is 36,198 ft. The greatest known depth in the Atlantic Ocean is 30,246 ft. What is the difference between the deepest point in the Atlantic Ocean and the deepest point in the Pacific Ocean?

44. A diver from a seaside cliff went a vertical distance of 67 ft before coming up to the surface of the water. If the elevation of the cliff is 49 ft, to what depth did he go in the sea?

45. A quiz show contestant starts her second day on the show with 500 points. On the first round, she loses 700 points. On the second round, she gains 850 points. How many points does she have after the second round?

Name _____   Date _____

Study Guide
For use with Section 3

A Call for Help   Integer Addition and Subtraction

GOAL   **LEARN HOW TO:** • use a model to work with integers
                              • add integers
                              • subtract integers
        AS YOU: • take and analyze hikes along a number line
                    • explore wind-chill temperatures

Exploration 1: Modeling Integer Operations

Number-Line Models

You can think of addition and subtraction as hikes on a number line.

Example

Find the sum $3 + (-5)$.

Sample Response

Start at 3, facing in the positive direction. Move backward 5 units.

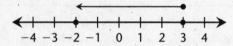

So, $3 + (-5) = -2$.

Exploration 2: Adding Integers

To add two integers with the *same sign*, add the absolute values of the integers. The sum has the same sign as the integers you are adding. For example, $9 + 3 = 12$ and $-5 + (-3) = -8$.

To add two integers that have *different signs*, subtract the lesser absolute value from the greater one. The sum has the same sign as the integer with the greater absolute value. For example, $2 + (-3) = -1$ and $-5 + 9 = 4$.

The sum of *0 and a number* is that number. For example, $0 + 6 = 6$ and $-3 + 0 = -3$.

The sum of *a number and its opposite* is 0. For example, $8 + (-8) = 0$.

Name _____ Date _____

 **Study Guide**
For use with Section 3

Properties of Addition

The **commutative property of addition** says that you can change the order of numbers in an addition problem and still get the same sum.

> **Example**
>
> $8 + 3 = 11$ and $3 + 8 = 11$
>
> $-7 + 2 = -5$ and $2 + (-7) = -5$
>
> $-3 + (-4) = -7$ and $-4 + (-3) = -7$

The **associative property of addition** says that you can change the grouping when you add numbers and still get the same sum.

> **Example**
>
> $3 + (4 + 5) = 3 + 9 = 12$ and $(3 + 4) + 5 = 7 + 5 = 12$
>
> $-5 + [4 + (-3)] = -5 + 1 = -4$ and $[-5 + 4] + (-3) = -1 + (-3) = -4$

Exploration 3: Subtracting Integers

You can rewrite a subtraction problem as an addition problem. To subtract an integer, add its opposite.

> **Example**
>
> Find each difference.
>
> **a.** $4 - (-7)$ **b.** $3 - 9$
>
> ■ **Sample Response** ■
>
> **a.** Rewrite the subtraction problem as an addition problem and then add.
>
> $4 - (-7) = 4 + 7$ ← Add the opposite of -7.
>
> $\qquad\qquad = 11$
>
> **b.** Rewrite the subtraction problem as an addition problem and then add.
>
> $3 - 9 = 3 + (-9)$ ← Add the opposite of 9.
>
> $\qquad\quad = -6$

Name _____   Date _____

Study Guide: Practice & Application Exercises

For use with Section 3

Exploration 1

A hiker on a number line follows each set of directions. Determine where the hiker will finish. Record the moves as an addition problem with its sum or as a subtraction problem with its difference.

1. Start at –5. Face the positive direction. Move backward 2 units.

2. Start at 3. Face the negative direction. Move forward 4 units.

3. Start at –1. Face the negative direction. Move backward 2 units.

Exploration 2

Find each sum.

4. $-4 + (-2)$ 5. $-5 + 0$ 6. $7 + 5$

7. $-13 + (-18)$ 8. $-9 + 5 + (-3)$ 9. $5 + 0 + (-5)$

Mental Math **Find each sum mentally. Use properties of addition.**

10. $-7 + 0 + (-5) + 7$ 11. $9 + (-4) + (-3) + 4 + (-6)$

12. $-8 + 5 + 13 + 0 + (-2)$ 13. $3 + (-14) + (-8) + 5$

For Exercises 14–19, evaluate each expression. Circle the expressions that have the same value.

14. $9 + 3 + 4 + (-8)$ 15. $7 + (-11) + 5 + (-3)$

16. $3 + 9 + (-8) + 4$ 17. $1 + 0 + (-10) + 11$

18. $0 + 11 + 1 + (-10)$ 19. $(-11) + (-3) + 5 + 7$

Exploration 3

For Exercises 20–27, rewrite each subtraction problem as the related addition problem that has the same answer. Then solve.

20. $9 - 5$ 21. $-5 - (-8)$ 22. $0 - (-3)$ 23. $8 - (-2)$

24. $-12 - 3$ 25. $2 - 4$ 26. $-2 - 8$ 27. $-1 - (-3)$

28. Find the difference $-6 - (-5)$.

Name _____ Date _____

Quick Quiz
For use after Section 3

1. Find each sum.

   a. $-12 + 8$ **b.** $84 + (-84)$ **c.** $-15 + (-15)$

2. Rewrite $2 - (-3)$ as the related addition problem that has the same answer.

3. Find each difference.

   a. $-20 - 41$ **b.** $13 - 18$ **c.** $-90 - (-4)$

4. From $-6°F$ at 6:00 A.M., the temperature rose $28°$ then fell $35°$ by 9:00 P.M.
   Write and evaluate an addition expression to model the situation.

5. Fill in each blank to make a true statement.

   a. $-5 - (\underline{})$ is negative.

   b. $-5 - (\underline{})$ is positive.

   c. $-5 - (\underline{})$ is zero.

Name _____   Date _____

For Questions 1–4 use the diagram at the right.

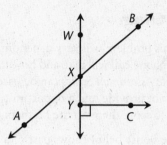

1. Name two rays that pass through point X.

2. Find the measure of $\angle AXW$.

3. Name and find the measure of an angle supplementary to $\angle AXW$.

4. Draw an angle complementary to $\angle WXB$.

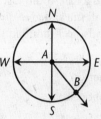

5. Use a protractor to find the heading shown in the compass diagram. What would the heading be if you were flying from town A to town B?

Find the opposite of each integer.

6. 27

7. –13

Find the absolute value of each integer.

8. $|-24|$

9. $|81|$

Replace each _____ with >, <, or =.

10. $-81 \_\_\_\_ 22$ 11. $|-4| \_\_\_\_ -5$ 12. $-|-3| \_\_\_\_ -3$

13. Plot each point on a coordinate plane:
    $A(4, -6), B(2, 3), C(-4, -4), D(5, 0), E(-1, 2)$.

14. In three plays, a football team gains 11 yd, loses 18 yd, and gains 3 yd. Write and evaluate an addition expression to model the situation.

Evaluate each expression.

15. $-90 + (-8)$ 16. $16 - 22$ 17. $-3 + 14$ 18. $5 + (-17)$

Write each product in exponential form and standard form.

19. $5 \cdot 5 \cdot 5 \cdot 5$

20. $7 \cdot 7 \cdot 7$

Evaluate each expression without using a calculator.

21. $120 \div 3 + 5 - 2 \cdot 10$

22. $(5^2 + 2 \cdot 4 - 17) \div 8$

Solution Guide: Textbook E²

For use with E² on textbook page 44

A Phone Chain

Solutions to this problem will vary depending on the amount of time students estimate each phone call will take and how the calls are made. All of the *Math Thematics Assessment Scales* can be used to assess students' solutions, but the problem does not provide much opportunity to use mathematical vocabulary, so you may not want to score them on the Mathematical Language Scale.

Each sample response below shows part of a student's solution.

Partial Solution

I decided a call would last about 30 seconds. I got 30 seconds by having my friend call me and give directions about where to meet and stuff. It took about 27 seconds, so I rounded to 30. My approach was to draw a diagram.

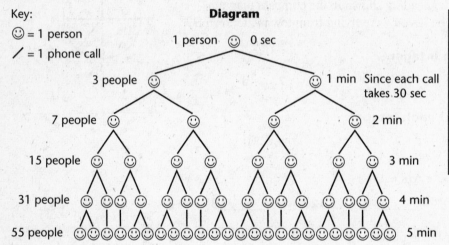

Level	Total number called	Total time
1	1	0 sec
2	3	1 min
3	7	2 min
4	15	3 min
5	31	4 min
6	55	5 min

My solution to this problem is that it takes 5 minutes for the phone chain to finish.

Partial Solution

I decided a call would take about 30 seconds and that people would start making their calls as soon as they were called. I drew a diagram of the calls.

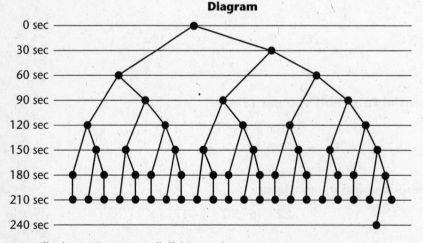

Time	People called	Total number called
0	1	1
30 sec	1	2
1 min	2	4
90 sec	3	7
2 min	5	12
150 sec	8	20
3 min	13	33
210 sec	21	54
4 min	1	55

It will take 4 minutes to call all 55 people.

Name _____   Date _____

Format for an E² Solution
For use with Book 2

Include the following three main headings in the write-up of
your E² solution.

Problem Statement

Write out the problem in your own words.

Problem Solving Procedure

Include the following in this section of your write-up.

Work
- Show all of the work you did to solve the problem.
- Include any tables, charts, graphs, diagrams, models, drawings, or equations that helped you solve the problem.

Explanation
- Give a step-by-step explanation of what you did to solve the problem.
- Identify the problem solving strategies you used and explain why you chose them.
- Use correct mathematical vocabulary and symbols wherever they are needed.
- Explain any changes you made in your thinking.
- Explain why your answer makes sense.
- You may use tables, charts, graphs, diagrams, models, drawings, and equations to help explain your solution.
- Check your solution or verify it by solving the problem another way.

Connections
- Explain how this problem is like other problems you have solved.
- Explain how this problem relates to a real-world situation or another mathematical idea.
- Try to extend the solution to other problems that are like this one.
- Try to find a rule that will work for any case of the problem.

Conclusion

Include the following in this section of your write-up.

Answer
- Write your answer to the problem.
- Be sure you answered the question or questions in the problem and clearly described your solution.

Learning
- You may include more than one response.
- Summarize what you learned from solving the problem.

Sample Scoring Profiles for an E² Solution

For use with Book 2

Excellent Response (A)

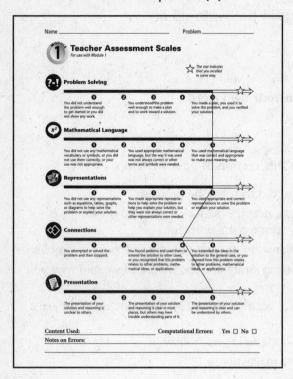

Good Response (B)

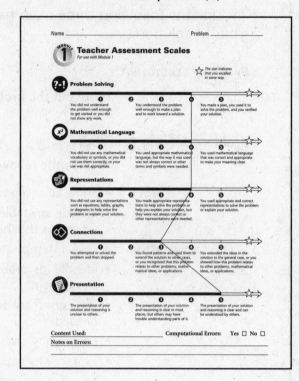

Developing Response (C)

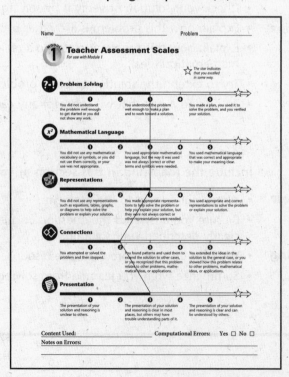

Math Thematics, Book 2
Teacher's Resource Book, Modules 1 and 2

Student Sample 1: Megan's E² Solution

For use with Book 2

<u>Things to decide on:</u>
• 1 call, I think, will take about 25 seconds. (The way I got
  25 seconds is my friend called me and we timed it. She gave me
  directions and told me where to meet and stuff and it took
  23 seconds so I rounded it to 25 seconds.)
• Everybody calls their person right then.
• Some of the calls do not go through the first time, so I am going
  to add some extra time (about 5 minutes to the total time I get).

<u>Estimate:</u> I think it will take about 15 + 5 = 20 minutes. I rounded
55 off to 60. I know part or half of the calls will be made at the
same time. So half of 60 is 30 and half of 30 is 15, so I did half
twice since a call takes about 30 seconds (I rounded 25 off to 30)
instead of 1 minute. So 15 for the calls plus my extra time
equals 20 minutes (estimate).

I am going to do a drawing for only part of the chain. Let's say
for $\frac{1}{5}$ of it or about 11 people. (Solve a simpler problem strategy.)

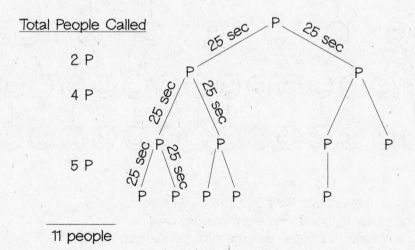

Key: P = phone call or person

For 11 people

Total People Called

2 P

4 P

5 P

Total Time

= 50 sec total

= 50 sec because
  the call is made
  together.

= 50 seconds

_____
11 people

_____
150 seconds

150 seconds
x   5 times this happens
―――――――――――
750 seconds

$$\begin{array}{r} 12.5 \\ 60{\overline{\smash{\big)}\,750}} \\ \underline{60} \\ 150 \\ \underline{120} \\ 300 \end{array}$$

= 13 minutes plus 5 minutes
  I said to add = 18 minutes
  total time. My estimate
  was close.

Student Sample 2: John's E^2 Solution
For use with Book 2

Problem Statement — Determine the least amount of time it would take using a phone chain to notify all of the members in a 55-person search and rescue team.

Problem Solving Procedure — How I approached this project was by drawing a diagram of each person calling the two people each person was assigned. I solved it this way so I could see the amount of minutes and the amount of people it took.

DIAGRAM

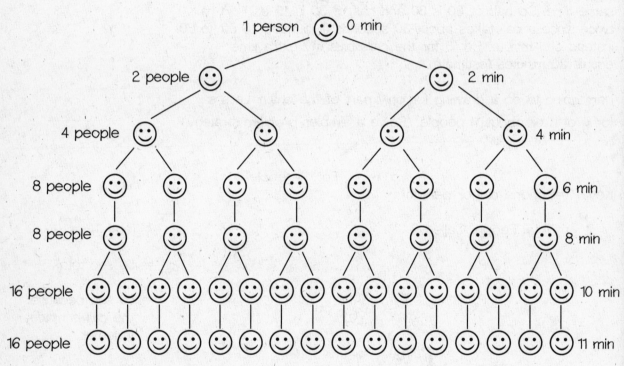

Conclusion — My solution to this project was that it took eleven minutes flat for the phone chain to finish. But eight people only had to call one person, and sixteen people only had to call sixteen people. What I had to consider as I solved the problem was that if I came up with an extreme answer the person that was lost might have been in serious danger by now.

Extension — To extend this project, I found a phone tree that was given to the parents in my sister's class. I see how you need to understand a phone chain for a real-world situation.

Name _____   Date _____

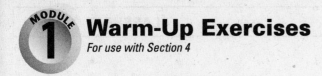

Warm-Up Exercises
For use with Section 4

Evaluate each expression.

1. $16 - 5 \cdot 7$

2. $12 \cdot 2 + 3 \cdot (-5)$

3. $8 - 2 \cdot (-4)$

Find the distance traveled by a car going 70 miles per hour for the given time.

4. 1 hour

5. 2 hours

6. 3 hours

7. 3.5 hours

ANSWERS

1. -19 2. 9   3. 16   4. 70 mi   5. 140 mi   6. 210 mi   7. 245 mi

Name _____   Date _____

Location Table (Use with Question 13 on page 49.)

Directions Complete the table to show the ambulance's location (mile marker)
at various times. Use the information in the diagram on page 49.

Ambulance Location								
Travel time (minutes)	0	4	8	12	16	20	24	t
Location (mile marker)	10	14						m

....

Location Grid (Use with Question 15 on page 49 and Questions 17–19
on page 50.)

Directions

• Plot the values from the table above in the grid below.

• Draw a line through the points to the edge of the grid.

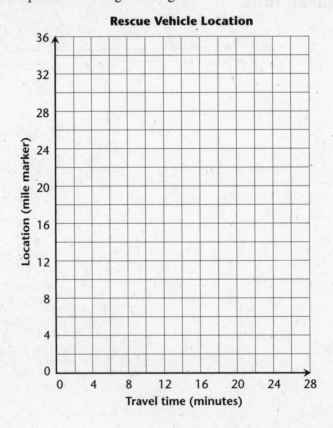

Rescue Vehicle Location

Name _____ Date _____

Practice and Applications

For use with Section 4

For use with Exploration 1

1. a. Nita started at her home and has driven at a steady speed for 2 hours. She has driven 110 miles. What is Nita's rate of speed?

b. Suppose Nita keeps the same speed for the whole trip. Complete the table of the distances driven in 1, 2, 3, 4, and 5 hours.

c. Write an equation relating Nita's distance driven to her travel time.

d. Nita is going to Destin, which is 550 miles from her home. How many hours does it take her to drive from her home to Destin?

Hours driven	Miles traveled
1	
2	
3	
4	
5	

e. What does the expression $550 - 55t$ model?

f. What values of t make sense for the expression in part (e)?

Choose the letter of the expression that models each situation.

2. An amusement park charges $3 to enter and $2 for each ride. What is the price of going to the park and riding on k rides?

   A. $2k$ **B.** $2k - 3$ **C.** $3 + 2k$

3. Mr. Anderson gets his brakes checked every 6 months. How many times does he get his brakes checked over a period of y years?

   A. $2y$ **B.** $6y$ **C.** $2y - 6$

Evaluate each expression when $x = 5$, $y = -3$, and $z = 6$.

4. $10x$ **5.** $2z + y$ **6.** $y - x$

7. $60 \div x$ **8.** $y + 7x$ **9.** $5z - y$

10. $y + xz$ **11.** $y - xz$ **12.** $2x - 4z$

13. a. Describe a situation that can be modeled by the expression $25q$.

b. Make a table that shows the values of the expression $25q$ for $q = 1$, $q = 2$, $q = 3$, and $q = 4$.

(continued)

Name _____ Date _____

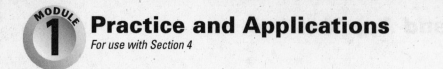

Practice and Applications

For use with Section 4

For use with Exploration 2

Copy and complete the table of values for each equation. Then graph each equation in a coordinate plane.

14. $y = x - 6$

x	−2	−1	0	1	2
y					

15. $y = x + 4$

x	−2	−1	0	1	2
y					

16. $y = 7 - x$

x	−2	−1	0	1	2
y					

17. $y = x + 5$

x	−2	−1	0	1	2
y					

Make a table of values for each equation. Then graph the equation in a coordinate plane.

18. $y = 3 - x$ **19.** $y = x + 9$ **20.** $y = 8 - x$

21. Linda borrowed some money to buy new software for her computer. Mike borrowed money for a sound system. The graph shows how they paid back their loans.

    a. How much did each person borrow? How does the graph show this information?

    b. How much did Linda pay back each month? How does the graph show this?

    c. How much did Mike pay back each month?

    d. Make tables to show how Linda and Mike paid back their loans.

    e. For each person, write an equation that describes how his or her loan was repaid. Tell what each variable represents.

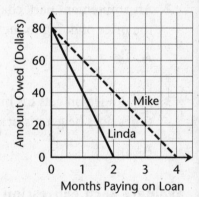

Use each graph to make a table of values of *x* and *y*. Then write an equation to model the relationship between *x* and *y*.

22.

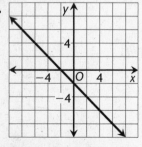

23.

Math Thematics, Book 2
Teacher's Resource Book, Modules 1 and 2

Name _____ Date _____

Study Guide

For use with Section 4

Urban Rescue   Function Models

GOAL **LEARN HOW TO:** • model a function with a table or an equation
• evaluate expressions with variables
• model a function with a graph

AS YOU: • explore distance, rate, and time
• choose between emergency vehicles

Exploration 1: Modeling a Function

Evaluating Expressions

An **expression** is a mathematical phrase containing numbers, operation
symbols, and **variables**—quantities that are unknown or that change.
To **evaluate** an expression that has a variable, substitute a value for the
variable and perform the operations. When two expressions are equal, you
can write an **equation** to express the relationship.

Variables

a t x

Expressions

$4 + 5$
$9x - 2$

Example

A hiker on a 50 mi journey has traveled for t hr at r mi per hr. Find the
distance left to hike after 12 hr at an average rate of 2 mi/hr.

▦ Sample Response ▦

Distance, rate, and time are related by the formula *distance traveled = rate • time*.
So, the distance traveled in t hours at r miles per hour is the product rt.

Therefore, an expression for the distance left to hike is $50 - rt$. Evaluate this expression
for $r = 2$ and $t = 12$.

$$50 - rt = 50 - 2 \cdot 12 \qquad \leftarrow \text{Substitute 2 for } r \text{ and 12 for } t.$$
$$= 50 - 24 = 26$$

The hiker has 26 mi left to travel.

Modeling Functions

A **function** is a relationship between input and output. For each input,
there is exactly one output. Making a table and writing an equation are
two ways to model a function. For example, you can make a table and
an equation to model the following function: A number y is 3 more than
twice another number x.

Table:

Input x	0	1	2	3	4
Output y	3	5	7	9	11

Equation: $y = 2x + 3$

Name _____   Date _____

 **Study Guide**
For use with Section 4

Exploration 2: Graphing a Function

A function can also be modeled using a graph.

Example

A festival sold tickets for a concert at \$2 each. A local company has agreed to donate an additional \$1 for each ticket sold. Model the relationship between the number of tickets sold and the amount of money collected using a table, an equation, and a graph. Then find out how much money is collected if 450 tickets are sold.

▌ Sample Response ▌

Make a table to show the relationship between the number of tickets sold (n) and the amount of money collected (c) for these values: 1, 2, 3, and n.

Tickets sold	Amount collected (\$)
1	3
2	6
3	9
n	c

Write an equation to model the relationship between the number of tickets sold and the amount collected.

$c = 3n$

Make a graph of the equation using the values in the table.

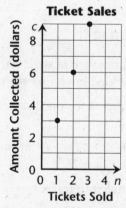

Use the equation to determine how much money is collected if 450 tickets are sold.

$c = 3n$
  $= 3(450)$ ← Replace n with 450.
  $= 1350$

For 450 tickets, \$1350 is collected.

Name _____   Date _____

Study Guide: Practice & Application Exercises
For use with Section 4

Exploration 1

1. Choose the letter of the expression that models this situation. The price of a book is m dollars. What is the price after a $1.50 decrease?

   A. $m + \$1.50$ **B.** $m - \$1.50$ **C.** $\$1.50 \div m$

2. Write an expression that models this situation.
Larry is 2 years older than Fran. Fran is t years old. How old is Larry?

Evaluate each expression when $a = 2$, $b = -2$, and $c = 3$.

3. $30a$ **4.** $6b$ **5.** $45 \div c$

6. $4b + 5$ **7.** $-3a - 11$ **8.** $b + 3c + a$

Exploration 2

For Exercises 9 and 10, copy and complete the table of values for each equation. Then graph each equation in a coordinate plane.

9. $y = x + (-2)$ **10.** $y = 2x - 1$

x	-2	-1	0	1	2
y	?	?	?	?	?

x	-10	-5	0	5	10
y	?	?	?	?	?

11. Describe a situation that can be modeled by the equation $y = x - 4$. Then make a table of values for the equation and graph the equation in a coordinate plane.

12. Your family visited cousins who live 600 mi from your home. You drove at an average rate of 50 mi/hr.

  a. Make a table showing the distances traveled by your family after 2, 4, 6, 8, 10, and 12 hours.

  b. Write an equation to model the distance traveled d in relation to travel time t.

  c. Graph the data from your table in part (a) on graph paper. Label each axis with reasonable values. Include axis titles and a graph title.

  d. Your family stopped for lunch after driving for 5 hours. How many miles had you traveled by this point?

  e. Explain the method you used to answer part (d).

Name _____   Date _____

Quick Quiz
For use after Section 4

1. Emily spends d dollars for dinner and m dollars for a movie. Write an expression that represents how much Emily spends in all.

2. Evaluate $a^2 + b$ when $a = 4$ and $b = -5$.

3. It costs $5 for admission to an amusement park and $1.50 per ride. Write an equation to model the relationship between the number of rides taken n and the total cost c.

4. Copy and complete the table of values for $y = 3x + 1$. Then graph the equation in a coordinate plane.

x	y
-2	
-1	
0	
1	
2	
3	

5. Write an expression that models the following situation: The speed limit on a stretch of highway is x mi/hr. If a policeman travels 15 mi/hr above the speed limit, how far will he go in 3 hr?

Name _____   Date _____

Warm-Up Exercises
For use with Section 5

Use mental math to solve each equation.

1. $n + 6 = 10$

2. $27 - p = 14$

3. $r \cdot 7 = 42$

4. $44 \div y = 4$

5. $9 \cdot b = 72$

6. $\dfrac{x}{4} = 20$

ANSWERS

1. $n = 4$ 2. $p = 13$ 3. $r = 6$ 4. $y = 11$ 5. $b = 8$ 6. $x = 80$

Name _____ Date _____

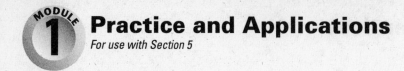

Practice and Applications
For use with Section 5

For use with Exploration 1

Write an addition equation to model each situation.

1. Sharlene has done 6 of her 10 homework problems.

2. Of the 23 mineral samples in Yoshi's collection, 4 are clear quartz.

Write a subtraction equation to model each situation.

3. The temperature dropped to –3°F after an afternoon high of 17°F.

4. A dentist sees only 36 patients, since 7 people cancelled appointments.

For use with Exploration 2

a. Write an equation that the model represents.

b. Solve the equation you wrote in part (a).

5.

$$\boxed{+} \; + \; \begin{array}{|c|c|c|}\hline + & + \\\hline + & + & + \\\hline\end{array} \; = \; \begin{array}{|c|c|c|c|c|c|}\hline + & + & + & + & + & + \\\hline + & + & + & + & + & + \\\hline\end{array}$$

6. $\boxed{+} \; + \; \boxed{+\;+\;+\;+} \; = \; \boxed{+\;+\;+\;+\;+\;+\;+\;+}$

For use with Exploration 3

Solve algebraically. Check each solution.

7. $k - 19 = -80$

8. $a + 8 = 53$

9. $380 = 10k$

10. $-15 + t = 24$

11. $12 = \dfrac{y}{6}$

12. $-17 = b + 50$

13. $x - 5 = 10$

14. $4x = 16$

15. $\dfrac{1}{3}x = 9$

For Exercises 13–18, tell whether the given value of the variable is a solution of the equation.

16. $a - 14 = 30; a = 16$

17. $-9 + b = -4; b = 5$

18. $x - (-7) = 26; x = 19$

19. $w + 5 = -30; w = -35$

20. $k - 8 = -8; k = 16$

21. $51 + n = -61; n = 112$

Write an equation to model each situation. Then solve and check the equation.

22. Two angles are supplementary. The larger has a measure of 139°.

23. After rising 55 m, a submarine was 63 m below sea level.

24. Andrew saved $85, but the CD player he plans to buy is $160.

Math Thematics, Book 2
Teacher's Resource Book, Modules 1 and 2

Name _____   Date _____

 **Study Guide**
For use with Section 5

Searching for a Solution   One-Step Equations

GOAL   **LEARN HOW TO:** • write and solve one-step equations
                                    • use inverse operations to solve one-step equations

         AS YOU: • examine search and rescue situations
                     • model equations with algebra tiles
                     • explore weight limits for a backpack

Exploration 1: Representing Situations

You can represent a situation in many ways. *Verbal statements* can help you
understand a problem by using words. *Balance models* can help you visualize
an equation and remember that both sides represent the same amount.
Equations use numbers, variables, and operations to describe a variety of
situations.

Exploration 2: Modeling Equations

A value of a variable that makes an equation true is a **solution of the
equation**. The process of finding solutions is called **solving an equation**.
Equations that have the same solutions are called **equivalent equations**.

Algebra tile models can help you solve an equation. Two algebra tiles, or
numbers, form a **zero pair** if the sum of their values is zero. For example, the
numbers 6 and –6 form a zero pair because $6 + (–6) = 0$.

Example

Model this situation: Sherry has 6 colors of model paint. Together, Sherry and Derrick
have 11 colors. How many colors does Derrick have?

| verbal statement: | Sherry's 6 colors | plus | Derrick's colors | equals | number of colors they have together |

| equation: | 6 | + | x | = | 11 |

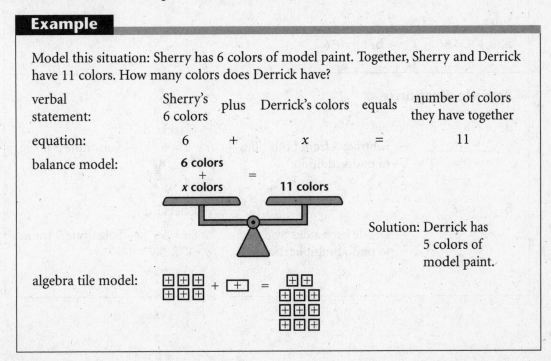

balance model: 6 colors + x colors   =   11 colors

Solution: Derrick has 5 colors of model paint.

algebra tile model:

Name _____ Date _____

 **Study Guide**
For use with Section 5

Exploration 3: Using Inverse Operations

Using Inverse Operations to Solve

Addition and subtraction are **inverse operations**. They "undo" each other. Multiplication and division are also inverse operations.

When you use symbols and variables to solve an equation, you are solving the equation *algebraically*.

To solve an equation, remember these ideas:

• The goal is to get the variable alone on one side of the equation.

• Use inverse operations to "undo" one another.

• The **properties of equality** (Addition Property of Equality, Subtraction Property of Equality, Multiplication Property of Equality, and Division Property of Equality) state that any operation done on one side of an equation must also be done on the other side to keep the equation balanced.

• Check that your solution is correct by substituting the value for the variable into the equation.

• If necessary, use tiles to model the equation.

Example

Solve.

a. $n + 5 = 8$ **b.** $8n = 56$

■ Sample Response ■

a.
$$n + 5 = 8$$
$$\underline{-5 = -5} \quad \leftarrow \text{Subtract 5 from both sides}$$
$$n + 0 = 3 \qquad \text{to undo addition.}$$
$$n = 3$$

Check:
$$n + 5 = 8 \quad \leftarrow \text{Substitute 3 for } n.$$
$$3 + 5 \overset{?}{=} 8$$
$$8 = 8 \checkmark$$

b. $8n = 56$
$$\frac{8n}{8} = \frac{56}{8} \quad \leftarrow \text{Divide both sides by 8}$$
$$n = 7 \qquad \text{to undo multiplication.}$$

Check:
$$8n = 56 \quad \leftarrow \text{Substitute 7 for } n.$$
$$8 \cdot 7 \overset{?}{=} 56$$
$$56 = 56 \checkmark$$

Name _____ Date _____

Study Guide: Practice & Application Exercises

For use with Section 5

Exploration 1

1. Write an equation to model this situation: Dorothy enrolled 36 new newspaper customers raising her total subscriptions to 78. Use one variable and tell what it represents.

2. Write an equation to model this situation: Jacob can run at a rate of 5 miles in one hour. He can bike 3 times as fast as he can run. Use one variable and tell what it represents.

Exploration 2

3. Write the equation represented by the model at the right.

   $$\boxed{+} \; + \; \begin{array}{ccc}\boxplus&\boxplus&\boxplus\\\boxplus&\boxplus&\boxplus\end{array} \; = \; \begin{array}{cccc}\boxplus&\boxplus&\boxplus&\boxplus\\\boxplus&\boxplus&\boxplus&\boxplus\end{array}$$

4. **Open-ended** Describe a situation that can be modeled by the equation $x - 4 = 7$. Be sure to tell what the variable represents.

5. Make an algebra tile model that represents $x - 2 = 5$. Then use the model to help you find the solution.

Exploration 3

For Exercises 6–17, solve algebraically. Check each solution.

6. $x - (-8) = -6$

7. $45 = 34 + t$

8. $y - 25 = -16$

9. $n + (-5) = 18$

10. $k - 19 = 13$

11. $49 = -5 + g$

12. $8 = 9 + c$

13. $0 = y - (-4)$

14. $w + 6 = 27$

15. $x - (-7) = 10$

16. $\frac{1}{6}x = 2$

17. $x + 10 = 11$

For Exercises 18–23, state the property of equality you would use to solve each equation. Then solve.

18. $2x = 8$

19. $5x = 25$

20. $x - 1 = -12$

21. $x + (-4) = 3$

22. $4 = \frac{1}{3}x$

23. $18 = 3x$

24. Is 5 a solution of the equation $-9 + n = 4$? Explain.

Name _____ Date _____

1. Write an equation represented by the algebra tile model.

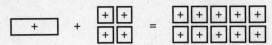

2. Write an addition or subtraction equation to model the following situation. Use one variable and tell what it represents.

   During a flu epidemic 14 students were absent, leaving only 11 in the class.

3. Solve.

   a. $-20 + n = 32$ **b.** $4 = \frac{r}{23}$ **c.** $8k = 120$

4. Is 21 a solution of $-24 = m - 3$? Justify your answer.

5. Two angles are supplementary. One angle has a measure of 82°. Let d = the measure of the other angle.

   a. Write the related addition equation.

   b. Solve the equation you wrote in part (a).

Math Thematics, Book 2
Teacher's Resource Book, Modules 1 and 2

Name _____   Date _____

1 Practice and Applications
For use after Sections 1–5

For use with Section 1

1. Draw an angle with each measure. Then classify each angle as *acute*, *obtuse*, *right*, or *straight*.

    a. 90°   **b.** 25°   **c.** 160°

2. For each angle measure:
Find the measure of a supplementary angle.
Find the measure of a complementary angle, if possible.

    a. 75°   **b.** 98°   **c.** 112°

3. Evaluate each expression using the order of operations.

    a. $12 + 32 \div 4^2 \cdot 7$ **b.** $7 + [(3^2 - 2^2) - 3] \cdot 6$ **c.** $(3 + 4)^2 \cdot (25 - 15)^2$

    d. $\dfrac{18 \div (4 + 2)}{9 - 8}$ **e.** $4 + [(6 + 9) \div 3] + 7 - 2$ **f.** $\dfrac{(45 + 5) \div 5}{8 - 6}$

4. Use grouping symbols to make each statement true.

    a. $28 - 10 \div 6 = 3$ **b.** $8 + 2 \cdot 7 = 70$ **c.** $4^2 + 2^2 \div 4 = 5$

For use with Section 2

5. Rewrite each elevation using symbols instead of words.

    a. Gannett Peak, Wyoming: 13,804 ft above sea level   **b.** Bristol Bay, Alaska: at sea level

    c. New Orleans, Louisiana: 8 ft below sea level   **d.** Death Valley, California: 282 ft below sea level

6. Find the opposite and the absolute value of each integer.

    a. 0   **b.** 49   **c.** −68

    d. −235   **e.** −99   **f.** 400

7. Replace each ___?___ with > or <.

    a. 12 ___?___ 0 **b.** -6 ___?___ 6 **c.** $|-30|$ ___?___ $|-50|$

    d. $|14|$ ___?___ $|-11|$ **e.** $|-28|$ ___?___ $|45|$ **f.** -36 ___?___ -41

(continued)

Name _____ Date _____

Practice and Applications
For use after Sections 1–5

For use with Section 3

8. Find each sum or difference.

   a. $9 + (-16)$ **b.** $-5 + 25$ **c.** $5 + 28$

   d. $19 + (-19)$ **e.** $-15 - 9$ **f.** $-26 - (-60)$

For use with Section 4

9. Evaluate each expression when $x = 12$, $y = -4$, and $z = 6$.

   a. $2x - 21$ **b.** $y + 8z$ **c.** $5x - y$ **d.** $xz + y$

10. Copy and complete the table of values for each equation. Then graph each equation in the coordinate plane.

   a. $y = x - 5$

x	−10	−5	0	5	10
y	?	?	?	?	?

   b. $y = 2x + 1$

x	−2	−1	0	1	2
y	?	?	?	?	?

11. A bus travels at an average rate of 50 mi/hr.

   a. Make a table showing the distance traveled for travel times of 0, 1, 2, 3, 4, 5, and 6 hr.

   b. Write an equation to model the distance traveled d in relation to travel time t.

For use with Section 5

12. Write an addition equation and a subtraction equation to model each situation. Use one variable and tell what it represents.

   a. Diana has 38 marbles. She and her brother together have 75 marbles.

   b. Ramon needs 5 points in the last quarter of the game to tie his high score of 23 points.

13. Solve. Check each solution.

   a. $r - 17 = -11$ **b.** $82 = v - 61$ **c.** $-14 = n + 22$

   d. $9t = -81$ **e.** $\frac{x}{-6} = -21$ **f.** $12y = 144$

Math Thematics, Book 2
Teacher's Resource Book, Modules 1 and 2

Name _____ Date _____

Regional Map (Use with Questions 1–3 on page 75.)

Directions Use headings to plan your initial search strategy.

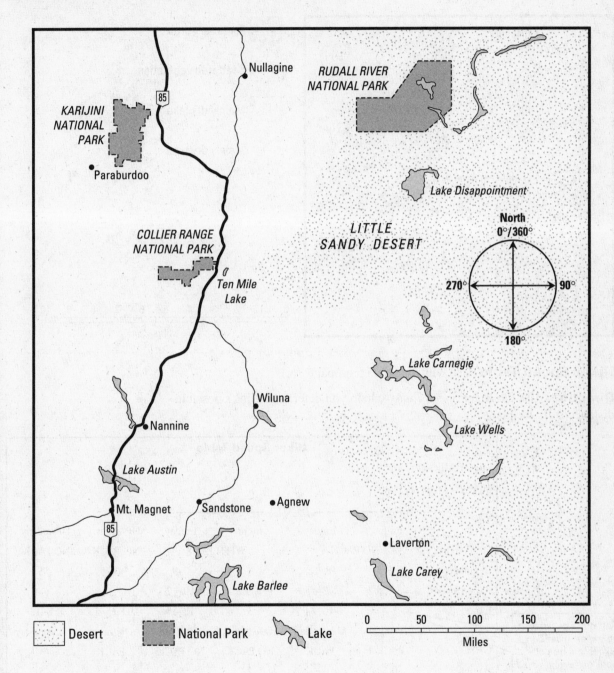

MODULE 1   **PROJECT LABSHEET** **B**

Map of Point Last Seen (Use with Questions 4, 6, and 7 on pages 75–76.)

Directions Use the *Map of Point Last Seen* as you refine your search plan.

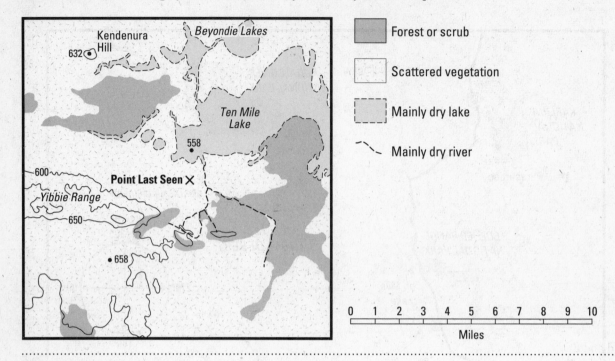

Hiker Speed Table (Use with Question 5 on page 76.)

Directions Use the *Hiker Speed Table* to help you determine Gina's possible distance from the plane.

Hiker Speed Table					
mi/hr = Miles per Hour					
mi/day = Miles per Day					
——————— LEVEL ———————					
mi/hr	mi/day	mi/hr	mi/day	UP-mi/hr	UP-mi/day
CATEGORY NO PACK		WITH PACK		NO PACK	NO PACK
Beginner	1.5–2	8–12	1–1.5	7–9	0.75	5
Experienced	2–2.5	12–15	1–5.2	10–12	1	6–8
Expert	3–4	16–24	3	12–18	1.25–2	8–12
	UP-mi/hr	UP-mi/day	DN-mi/hr	DN-mi/day	DN-mi/hr	DN-mi/day
CATEGORY	PACK	PACK	NO PACK	NO PACK	PACK	PACK
Beginner	0.5	3	2	7	1.5	5
Experienced	0.75	6	2–3	9–10	2	7
Expert	1–1.5	6–10	2.5–3.5	10–14	2–2.5	10

> Without a backpack, an expert hiker can hike 3 to 4 mi per hour on level ground.

> A beginner hiker with a backpack can hike 5 mi per day if he or she is heading downhill.

Math Thematics, Book 2
Teacher's Resource Book, Modules 1 and 2

1-60

MODULE 1   **PROJECT LABSHEET** **C**

Search Grid (Use with Question 8 on page 77.)

Directions Use the grid to find how long it took searcher S4 to find footprints in the mud at point F.

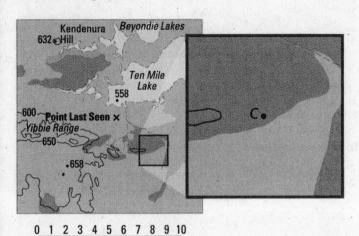
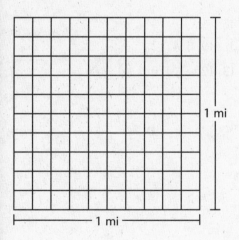

0 1 2 3 4 5 6 7 8 9 10
Miles

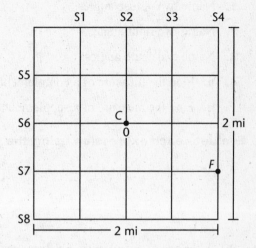

Revised Search Grid (Use with Question 9 on page 77.)

Directions Plot point F, your starting point, at the origin in the center of the grid and draw the paths that you think the searchers should follow based on the information in Question 9.

1 mi

1 mi

Name _____   Date _____

Test Form A
For use after Module 1

For Questions 1–4, use the diagram at the right.

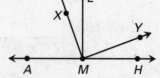

1. Name two obtuse angles.

2. Name two right angles.

3. Name two acute angles.

4. **a.** Find the measure of a complementary angle to ∠*YMH*.

   b. Find the measure of a supplementary angle to ∠*YMH*.

Evaluate each expression using the order of operations.

5. $4^2 + 10^3$

6. $\dfrac{40 + 2 \cdot 4}{10 + 2 \cdot 3}$

7. $36 \div (15 - 11) \cdot 9$

8. After heavy spring rains, a newspaper reported that the local river was within 4 ft of flooding over its banks. Use integers to describe this situation. Be sure to indicate what positive integers, negative integers, and zero represent.

9. Which list shows the integers in order from least to greatest?

   A. 0, 4, –7, 12, –13, –19   **B.** –7, –13, –19, 0, 4, 12

   C. –19, –13, –7, 0, 4, 12   **D.** –19, –13, 12, –7, 4, 0

10. Which integer has the least absolute value?

    A. –19   **B.** –7   **C.** 0   **D.** 4

11. Describe two items that have the following relationship:

    a. are parallel to each other

    b. are perpendicular to each other

Evaluate each expression.

12. $-4 + 12$ 13. $-7 + (-3)$ 14. $-8 - 17$ 15. $6 + (-3) - 10$

Test Form A
For use after Module 1

For Questions 16–19, refer to the coordinate plane at the right.
Write the coordinates of each point.

16. point *A*

17. point *D*

18. point *C*

19. point *F*

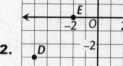

Evaluate each expression when *m* = 7, *a* = –3, *b* = –4, and *n* = 12.

20. $2m + a$

21. $n - 3m$

22. $7 - a$

23. A contractor is going to purchase steel pipe and plastic tubing for a building project. The steel pipe weighs 5 lb/ft and the plastic tubing weighs 2 lb/ft.

  a. Complete the table to show the weights of the different lengths of pipe and plastic tubing the contractor needs.

  b. Write an equation that shows the relationships between *L*, the length of the pipe or tubing, and *w*, the weight.

  c. Graph your equations from part (b) in the same coordinate plane. Draw lines connecting the points for each item.

Length (ft)	Weight (lb)	
	Steel pipe	Plastic Tubing
10		
20		
40		
50		
60		
L		

  d. Use your graph to find out how much more a 45 ft piece of steel pipe weighs than a 45 ft piece of tubing.

Solve and check.

24. $52 = 45 + x$

25. $\dfrac{m}{15} = 5$

26. $8f = 96$

27. $y - 8 = -27$

28. Elsa has 47 CDs. Last week she gave 9 CDs to a friend.

  a. Write an equation to model the situation. Identify the variable you use.

  b. Solve the equation.

Name _____   Date _____

Test Form B
For use after Module 1

For Questions 1–4, use the diagram at the right.

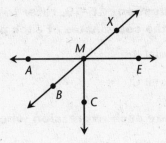

1. Name two obtuse angles.

2. Name two right angles.

3. Name two acute angles.

4. **a.** Find the measure of a complementary angle to $\angle XME$.

   b. Find the measure of a supplementary angle to $\angle XME$.

Evaluate each expression using the order of operations.

5. $3^2 + 4^3$

6. $\dfrac{20 + 4 \cdot 4}{10 - 2 \cdot 4}$

7. $60 \div (17 - 11) \cdot 10$

8. After heavy spring rains, a newspaper reported that the local river was within 7 ft of flooding over its banks. Use integers to describe this situation. Be sure to indicate what positive integers, negative integers, and zero represent.

9. Which list shows the integers in order from least to greatest?

   A. 0, 7, –9, 12, –13, –25   **B.** –9, –13, –25, 0, 7, 12

   C. –25, –13, –9, 0, 7, 12   **D.** –25, –13, 12, –9, 7, 0

10. Which integer has the least absolute value?

   A. –25   **B.** –9   **C.** 0   **D.** 7

11. Describe two items that have the following relationship:

   a. are parallel to each other

   b. are perpendicular to each other

Evaluate each expression.

12. $8 + (-7)$

13. $-3 + 11$

14. $-8 - 16$

15. $-9 + 13 - 8$

Test Form B
For use after Module 1

For Questions 16–19, refer to the coordinate plane at the right. Write the coordinates of each point.

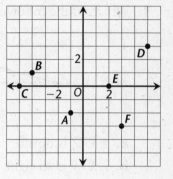

16. point A

17. point D

18. point C

19. point F

Evaluate each expression when $m = 7$, $a = -3$, $b = -4$, and $n = 12$.

20. $6m + a$

21. $b - 3n$

22. $7 - b$

23. A contractor is going to purchase steel pipe and plastic tubing for a building project. The steel pipe weighs 15 lb/yd and the plastic tubing weighs 6 lb/yd.

    a. Complete the table to show the weights of the different lengths of pipe and plastic tubing the contractor needs.

    b. Write an equation that shows the relationships between L, the length of the pipe or tubing, and w, the weight.

    c. Graph your equations from part (b) in the same coordinate plane. Draw lines connecting the points for each item.

Length (yd)	Weight (lb)	
	Steel pipe	Plastic Tubing
30		
60		
120		
150		
180		
L		

    d. Use your graph to find out how much more a 45 yd piece of steel pipe weighs than a 45 yd piece of tubing.

Solve and check.

24. $39 = 15 + x$

25. $\dfrac{m}{12} = 4$

26. $4f = 76$

27. $y - 13 = -21$

28. Elsa has 39 CDs. Last week she gave 5 CDs to a friend.

    a. Write an equation to model the situation. Identify the variable you use.

    b. Solve the equation.

Name _____   Date _____

1. Which of the following statements is false?

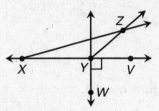

  a. ∠YXZ is obtuse.
  b. ∠XYV is straight.
  c. ∠ZYV is acute.
  d. ∠WYV is right.

2. Solve the equation $21x = 252$.
  a. 25.2   **b.** 20
  c. 18   **d.** 12

3. The deepest point in the world's oceans is 35,797 ft below sea level. Mt. Everest is 29,029 ft high. What is the difference between these two elevations?
  a. 6668 ft   **b.** 6768 ft
  c. 64,826 ft   **d.** 65,716 ft

4. What are the coordinates of point A?

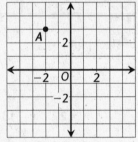

  a. $(-2, 3)$ **b.** $(-2, -3)$
  c. $(3, -2)$ **d.** $(-3, 2)$

5. Evaluate $-14 - (18 - 21)$.
  a. −11   **b.** −17
  c. −43   **d.** −53

6. Write an equation that models this sentence: Eight less than three times seven equals x.
  a. $8 - 3 \cdot 7 = x$
  b. $8(3 - 7) = x$
  c. $3(x - 8) = 7$
  d. $3 \cdot 7 - 8 = x$

7. Evaluate $a^2 - b + 4$ when $a = 5$ and $b = -2$.
  a. 4   **b.** 16
  c. 19   **d.** 31

8. ∠A and ∠B are complementary. The measure of ∠A is 20°. What is the measure of an angle that is supplementary to ∠B?
  a. 70°   **b.** 110°
  c. 140°   **d.** 160°

9. Predict the cost of 5 lb of apples.

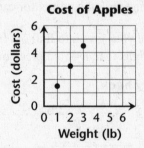

  a. $6.50   **b.** $7.00
  c. $7.50   **d.** $8.00

10. Evaluate $25 \cdot 3 - 20 + 60 \div 15$.
  a. 7   **b.** 35
  c. 59   **d.** 65

Name _____   Date _____

 Module Performance Assessment
For use after Module 1

A middle school class is thinking of two possible ways to raise money to buy new equipment for the school. One option is to sell raffle tickets for donated items. For every raffle ticket a student sells, the school will make a profit of $2. The other option is to sell $6 tickets to a fundraising performance. That performance will cost $175 (taken from the profits) to put on.

Step 1: The equation $6t - 175 = p$ describes the profit p the school makes from the fundraiser after selling t tickets. Evaluate the expression $6t - 175$ to find the value of p when $t = 15$.

Step 2: Construct a table of values to show how much profit the school would make if the class sold 10, 25, or 150 tickets for the fundraiser. What do negative values of p represent? What do positive values of p represent?

Step 3: Use the table you made in Step 2 to graph the equation $6t - 175 = p$ on a coordinate grid. Draw a line to connect the points. About how many tickets must the class sell to make a profit on the fundraiser?

Step 4: Write an equation to describe the relationship between the amount of money p the school makes after the class sells t tickets for the raffle. Construct a table of values for the equation and graph the results on the same coordinate grid you used in Step 3.

Step 5: Examine the graph. In which situation is the raffle a better idea? the fundraiser? Explain how the intersection of the lines relates to the effectiveness of each method for raising money for the school.

Step 6: Suppose the class decides to sell raffle tickets. They start with a roll of 300 tickets. After selling a certain number of tickets, 26 still remain. Write an equation to model the situation using a variable, and explain what the variable represents. Solve the equation to find how many tickets have been sold.

Contents

Book 2	Teacher's Resources for Module 2

Bright Ideas

Name _____ Date _____

Module Diagnostic Test

For use before Module 2

1. Which fraction below is equivalent to 0.37?   (Sec. 1)

    A. $\frac{3}{7}$ **B.** $\frac{37}{10}$ **C.** $\frac{37}{100}$ **D.** $\frac{37}{1000}$

2. Which decimal number below is greater than 1.053?   (Sec. 1)

    A. 1.05199   **B.** 1.06   **C.** 1.00531   **D.** 0.99

3. Which of the following represents 3^{-2} written in standard form?   (Sec. 1)

    A. $\frac{1}{9}$ **B.** $\frac{1}{6}$ **C.** -9 **D.** -6

4. 14,032 written in scientific notation is   (Sec. 1)

    A. $1.4032 \cdot 10^{-4}$ **B.** $14.032 \cdot 10^{3}$ **C.** $1.4032 \cdot 10^{-1}$ **D.** $1.4032 \cdot 10^{4}$

5. Which of the following represents the slope of the line shown at the right?   (Sec. 2)

    A. 3   **B.** $\frac{1}{3}$ **C.** 0   **D.** (3, 1)

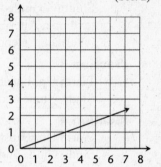

6. Make two line graphs of the data in the table using different vertical and horizontal scales. Label one graph to show that the price of this item is decreasing rapidly. Label the other graph to show that the price has remained about the same.

    (Sec. 2)

Year	Price
2002	$15
2003	$14.48
2004	$13.99
2005	$13.28
2006	$12.75
2007	$12.36

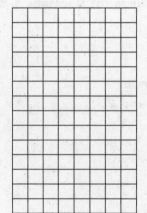

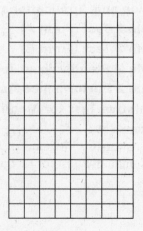

Name _____   Date _____

Module Diagnostic Test

For use before Module 2

7. a. Complete the table for the first 6 terms of the sequence: 3, 7, 11, 15, ...   (Sec. 3)

Term Number	1	2	3	4	5	6
Term	3	7	11	15		

   b. Write an equation for finding the terms of the sequence.

   c. Predict the 99th term of the sequence.

8. Which of the following expressions is equivalent to $6x + 2$?   (Sec. 3)

   A. $3(x + 2) + 2$ **B.** $6(x + 2)$ **C.** $6(x + 2) - 10$

9. Which of the following illustrates the distributive property of multiplication over addition?   (Sec. 3)

   A. $(13 + 10)2 = 26 + 20$ **B.** $5 \cdot 3 = 3 \cdot 5$
   C. $7 + (4 \cdot 2) = 7 + 8$ **D.** $5 \cdot 3 = 5 + 5 + 5$

10. Complete the next three steps in the 4-Step Approach to Problem Solving.   (Sec. 4)

   Step 1: Understand the Problem
   Step 2: _____
   Step 3: _____
   Step 4: _____

Use the spinner at the right for Questions 11–13.   (Sec. 5)

11. Kalli spun the spinner 39 times. Her results are shown in the table below. Find the experimental probability of each outcome.

Outcome	Frequency
blue	25
yellow	9
green	5

12. Find the theoretical probability of each outcome.

13. Suppose you spin the spinner 200 times. About how many times would you expect it to land on blue?

The Math Gazette
Bright Ideas

Sneak Preview!

Over the next several weeks in our mathematics class, we will be applying problem-solving and reasoning skills and developing pre-algebra, number, and probability concepts while completing a thematic unit on Bright Ideas. Some of the topics we will be discussing are:

▶ analyzing patterns in mathematics and nature

▶ investigating the number of Calories burned during exercise

▶ determining how likely events are to happen

Ask Your Student

According to the ancient Greeks, how many grains of sand would it take to fill the entire universe? (Sec. 1)

How can a graph be misleading? (Sec. 2)

What are the steps in the 4-step problem-solving approach? (Sec. 4)

What does a probability of $\frac{1}{6}$ mean? (Sec. 5)

Connections

Literature:
Students will read the poem *Smart*, by Shel Silverstein, and solve problems and puzzles from the book *In Code*, by Sarah Flannery. You may enjoy reading other Shel Silverstein poems with your student.

Science:
Students will investigate topics related to astronomy, including the orbits of comets and the size of the universe.

Recreation:
Students will explore how probability is involved in several popular board games.

Visual Arts:
Students will use graphs to display information and explore how the scales selected for a graph can affect the way that data appear.

E² Project

Following Section 2, students will have approximately one week to complete the Extended Exploration (E²), *The Painted Cube*. This project requires students to use spatial skills to determine the number of painted faces on small cubes cut from a larger cube that has been painted.

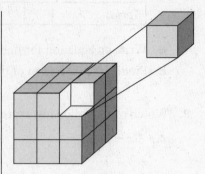

Students might need some of the following materials for the project:

▶ grid paper, scissors, and tape for constructing cubes

▶ wooden blocks or sugar cubes

Module Project

After completing the module, students will collect data to investigate how television advertisers try to influence people's choices. Students will use the data to make predictions and to determine whether some claims are valid. They will choose appropriate representations for the data to use in a presentation of what they learn.

Bright Ideas

Section Title	Mathematics Students Will Be Learning	Activities
1: New Notations	<ul><li>writing decimals as fractions</li><li>reading, writing, and comparing decimals</li><li>using integer exponents and writing numbers in scientific notation</li></ul>	<ul><li>play *Where's the Best Place* to review decimal place value</li><li>use a calculator to investigate scientific notation</li></ul>
2: Fuel for Your Body	<ul><li>choosing scales for graphs</li><li>graphing linear functions and finding the slopes of the lines</li><li>analyzing how the scale affects the appearance of a graph</li><li>using Assessment Scales to evaluate the use of representations in problem solving</li></ul>	<ul><li>graph equations for the number of Calories burned in various exercises</li><li>compare graphs with different scales to decide which best displays given data</li></ul>
3: Halley and His Comet	<ul><li>modeling sequences with tables, graphs, and equations</li><li>using the associative, commutative, and distributive properties to simplify expressions</li></ul>	<ul><li>use square tiles and graphs to analyze patterns</li><li>use square tiles to discover and model equivalent expressions</li></ul>
4: Young Problem Solvers	<ul><li>using a 4-step approach to problem solving</li><li>using problem-solving strategies</li><li>using Assessment Scales to evaluate problem solving and making connections</li></ul>	<ul><li>solve puzzles from the book *In Code* by Sarah Flannery</li><li>analyze a card trick</li></ul>
5: Likely or Unlikely?	<ul><li>determining the outcomes of an experiment</li><li>finding experimental and theoretical probabilities of events</li></ul>	<ul><li>use probabilities to develop a strategy for playing a game</li></ul>

Activities to do at Home

- Play *Where's the Best Place* with your student and compare strategies for playing the game. (After Sec. 1)

- Where are statistics used? Ask your student to look for examples of bar, line, and other graphs in newspapers, magazines, and on television and explain whether the graphs are appropriate and contain all the necessary information. (After Sec. 2)

- Look at the games you have at home and use experimental or theoretical probability to study the game, comparing theoretical and experimental probabilities of number cube rolls, spinners, and so on. (After Sec. 5)

Related Topics

You may want to discuss these related topics with your student:

 Astronomy

 Games of chance

 Television advertising

 Health and fitness

 Methods of assessing performance

Name _____   Problem _____

Teacher Assessment Scales

For use with Module 2

☆ *The star indicates that you excelled in some way.*

 ## Problem Solving

❶   **❷**   **❸**   **❹**   **❺**

❶	❸	❺
You did not understand the problem well enough to get started or you did not show any work.	You understood the problem well enough to make a plan and to work toward a solution.	You made a plan, you used it to solve the problem, and you verified your solution.

 ## Mathematical Language

❶   **❷**   **❸**   **❹**   **❺**

❶	❸	❺
You did not use any mathematical vocabulary or symbols, or you did not use them correctly, or your use was not appropriate.	You used appropriate mathematical language, but the way it was used was not always correct or other terms and symbols were needed.	You used mathematical language that was correct and appropriate to make your meaning clear.

 ## Representations

❶   **❷**   **❸**   **❹**   **❺**

❶	❸	❺
You did not use any representations such as equations, tables, graphs, or diagrams to help solve the problem or explain your solution.	You made appropriate representations to help solve the problem or help you explain your solution, but they were not always correct or other representations were needed.	You used appropriate and correct representations to solve the problem or explain your solution.

 ## Connections

❶   **❷**   **❸**   **❹**   **❺**

❶	❸	❺
You attempted or solved the problem and then stopped.	You found patterns and used them to extend the solution to other cases, or you recognized that this problem relates to other problems, mathematical ideas, or applications.	You extended the ideas in the solution to the general case, or you showed how this problem relates to other problems, mathematical ideas, or applications.

Presentation

❶   **❷**   **❸**   **❹**   **❺**

❶	❸	❺
The presentation of your solution and reasoning is unclear to others.	The presentation of your solution and reasoning is clear in most places, but others may have trouble understanding parts of it.	The presentation of your solution and reasoning is clear and can be understood by others.

Content Used: _____   **Computational Errors:**   Yes ☐   No ☐

Notes on Errors: _____

Name _____   Problem _____

Student Self-Assessment Scales
For use with Module 2

 If your score is in the shaded area, explain why on the back of this sheet and stop.

☆ The star indicates that you excelled in some way.

 ## Problem Solving

①   ②   ③   ④   ⑤

I did not understand the problem well enough to get started or I did not show any work.

I understood the problem well enough to make a plan and to work toward a solution.

I made a plan, I used it to solve the problem, and I verified my solution.

 ## Mathematical Language

①   ②   ③   ④   ⑤

I did not use any mathematical vocabulary or symbols, or I did not use them correctly, or my use was not appropriate.

I used appropriate mathematical language, but the way it was used was not always correct or other terms and symbols were needed.

I used mathematical language that was correct and appropriate to make my meaning clear.

 ## Representations

①   ②   ③   ④   ⑤

I did not use any representations such as equations, tables, graphs, or diagrams to help solve the problem or explain my solution.

I made appropriate representations to help solve the problem or help me explain my solution, but they were not always correct or other representations were needed.

I used appropriate and correct representations to solve the problem or explain my solution.

 ## Connections

①   ②   ③   ④   ⑤

I attempted or solved the problem and then stopped.

I found patterns and used them to extend the solution to other cases, or I recognized that this problem relates to other problems, mathematical ideas, or applications.

I extended the ideas in the solution to the general case, or I showed how this problem relates to other problems, mathematical ideas, or applications.

 ## Presentation

①   ②   ③   ④   ⑤

The presentation of my solution and reasoning is unclear to others.

The presentation of my solution and reasoning is clear in most places, but others may have trouble understanding parts of it.

The presentation of my solution and reasoning is clear and can be understood by others.

Warm-Up Exercises
For use with Section 1

State the place value of the given digit in the number 3,965,280.

1. 2

2. 3

3. 9

4. 0

5. 8

6. 5

ANSWERS

1. hundreds   2. millions   3. hundred thousands   4. ones   5. tens   6. thousands

Name _____ Date _____

Positive Powers of 10 Table
(Use with Question 15 on page 86.)

Directions Use multiplication to complete the table.

Exponential form	Standard form
10^1	10
10^2	100
10^3	1000
10^4	
10^5	
10^6	

Integer Powers of 10 Table (Use with Question 16 on page 86 and Questions 17 and 21 on page 87.)

Directions Use division to complete the table.

Exponential form	Standard form	
	Using decimals	Using fractions
10^3	1000	1000
10^2	100	100
10^1	10	10
10^0		
10^{-1}		$\frac{1}{10}$
10^{-2}	0.01	
10^{-3}		

Powers of 2 Table (Use with Questions 19 and 21 on page 87.)

Directions

- Use patterns, your knowledge of exponents, and a calculator to complete the second and third rows of the table. Write all fractions in lowest terms.

- In the last row, rewrite each fraction so the denominator is written in exponential form with base 2.

Enter [2] [y^x] [2] [+⊙-] [=].

Remember, $0.25 = \frac{25}{100} = \frac{1}{4}$.

Power of 2	2^5	2^4	2^3	2^2	2^1	2^0	2^{-1}	2^{-2}	2^{-3}	2^{-4}	2^{-5}
Standard form using decimals			8					0.25			
using fractions			$\frac{8}{1}$					$\frac{1}{4}$			
Denominator in exponential form								$\frac{1}{2^2}$			

MODULE 2   LABSHEET **1B**

Product Table (Use with Questions 26 and 27 on page 89.)

Directions

- Complete the table with the products that you know how to compute.

- Look for a pattern in the position of the decimal point and the digits in your answer. Use the pattern to complete the table.

Multiplication by Powers of 10
$235 \cdot 10^3$ =
$235 \cdot 10^2$ = $235 \cdot 100 = 23{,}500$
$235 \cdot 10^1$ =
$235 \cdot 10^0$ =
$235 \cdot 10^{-1}$ =
$235 \cdot 10^{-2}$ =
$235 \cdot 10^{-3}$ = $235 \cdot 0.001$ =

Math Thematics, Book 2
Teacher's Resource Book, Modules 1 and 2

Name _____   Date _____

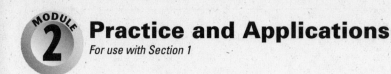

Practice and Applications
For use with Section 1

For use with Exploration 1

1. Write each number in words.

   a. 3284.15   **b.** 0.835   **c.** 5.025

   d. 2.003   **e.** 0.0103   **f.** 10.061

   g. 0.00205   **h.** 5.0001   **i.** 31.502

2. Write each number as a fraction or a mixed number.

   a. 0.73   **b.** 41.9   **c.** 0.305

   d. 0.0063   **e.** 1.0071   **f.** 4.36005

   g. 6.0804   **h.** 12.01012   **i.** 18.00026

   j. 0.002   **k.** 0.18   **l.** 14.6

   m. 2.125   **n.** 3.05   **o.** 10.105

   p. 6.50   **q.** 9.4   **r.** 7.225

3. Replace each ___?___ with >, <, or =.

   a. 0.36 ___?___ 0.036   **b.** 1.895 ___?___ 1.859   **c.** 0.209 ___?___ 0.3

   d. 14.091 ___?___ 14.101   **e.** 0.72 ___?___ 0.720   **f.** 8.61 ___?___ 8.612

   g. 42.7 ___?___ 4.27   **h.** 0.008 ___?___ 0.080   **i.** 0.518 ___?___ 0.517

   j. 0.39 ___?___ 0.391   **k.** 17.6 ___?___ 17.59   **l.** 0.25 ___?___ 0.205

   m. 0.032 ___?___ 0.0320   **n.** 0.46 ___?___ 0.416   **o.** 19.8 ___?___ 20.12

4. To pass inspection, a bolt must be between 0.45 and 0.55 cm wide.

   a. Which of the following bolts will pass inspection: 0.445, 0.521, 0.457, 0.553, 0.551, 0.459, 0.5, 0.508, 0.52, 0.46, and 0.533?

   b. Order the bolts that will pass inspection in order of increasing width.

(continued)

MODULE 2 — Practice and Applications
For use with Section 1

For use with Exploration 2

5. Write each power of ten in standard form.

    a. 10^3 **b.** 10^5 **c.** 10^0

    d. 10^{-2} **e.** 10^4 **f.** 10^{-3}

    g. 10^6 **h.** 10^{-4} **i.** 10^{-1}

6. Write each power as a fraction with its denominator in standard form.

    a. 2^{-5} **b.** 4^{-3} **c.** 9^{-2}

    d. 6^{-3} **e.** 15^{-2} **f.** 30^{-3}

7. Write each number in exponential form with base 10.

    a. 10,000,000   **b.** 0.1   **c.** 1000

    d. 0.00001   **e.** 1   **f.** 0.001

For use with Exploration 3

8. Write each product in standard form.

    a. $4.6 \cdot 10^4$ **b.** $16.35 \cdot 10^{-4}$ **c.** $14.2413 \cdot 10^3$

    d. $3.47 \cdot 10^4$ **e.** $0.0351 \cdot 10^3$ **f.** $231,467 \cdot 10^{-6}$

    g. $6215 \cdot 10^{-3}$ **h.** $0.0052 \cdot 10^5$ **i.** $2.41 \cdot 10^{-5}$

9. Write each number in scientific notation.

    a. 16,302   **b.** 0.0047   **c.** 6325.7

    d. 0.2416   **e.** 624,100   **f.** 0.000058

10. The polar diameter of Earth is $7.8998 \cdot 10^3$ mi. The mean diameter of Earth is $7.91752 \cdot 10^3$ mi.

    a. Write each diameter in standard form.

    b. Which diameter is greater?

Name _____ Date _____

Study Guide
For use with Section 1

Bright Ideas   Decimals and Exponents

GOAL **LEARN HOW TO:** • compare numbers using the decimal place value system
• write a decimal as a fraction
• use integer exponents to read and write numbers
• multiply decimals by powers of 10
• write numbers in scientific notation

AS YOU: • play a game with number squares
• explore powers of 10
• look at calculator displays

Exploration 1: Decimal Place Values

In the **decimal place** value system, the position of the digit in
a number determines its value.

The digits to the left of the decimal point form the whole number
part of the decimal number, while the digits to the right of the
decimal point form the fractional part.

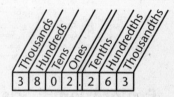

You can compare and order decimals by comparing digits with
the same place value, beginning at the left.

Example
Compare 3.507 and 3.52.

Sample Response

The ones and tenths digits are equal, so compare the hundredths digits.

Since $0 < 2$, therefore $3.507 < 3.52$.

You can write decimal numbers as fractions or mixed numbers.

Example
Write 3.23 as a fraction or mixed number.

Sample Response

3.23 means *three and twenty-three hundredths*. Hundredths means
"parts of a hundred," so the denominator is 100.

$3.23 = 3\frac{23}{100}$

Name _____ Date _____

Study Guide

For use with Section 1

Exploration 2: Integer Exponents

Positive and negative integers and zero can be used as exponents. A
number that can be written in exponential form is a **power** of the base.
The 0th power of any nonzero number is 1.

> ### Example
>
> **a.** Write 6^3 in standard form.   **b.** Write 5^{-4} as a fraction.
>
> ### Sample Response
>
> **a.** $6^3 = 6 \cdot 6 \cdot 6 = 216$ ← Read: "6 to the 3rd power (or 6 cubed) equals 216."
>
> **b.** $5^{-4} = \dfrac{1}{5^4} = \dfrac{1}{5 \cdot 5 \cdot 5 \cdot 5} = \dfrac{1}{625}$ ← Read: "5 to the negative 4th power equals $\dfrac{1}{625}$."

Exploration 3: Scientific Notation

Multiplying by Powers of Ten

When multiplying by powers of ten, the exponent can help you decide
where to place the decimal point.

> ### Example
>
> Write each product in standard form.
>
> **a.** $16.234 \cdot 10^2$ **b.** $16.234 \cdot 10^{-2}$
>
> ### Sample Response
>
> **a.** $16.234 \cdot 10^2 = 1623.4$ ← Move the decimal point **right** 2 places.
>
> **b.** $16.234 \cdot 10^{-2} = 0.16234$ ← Move the decimal point **left** 2 places.

Scientific Notation

Scientific notation is a way to write numbers as the product of a decimal
and a power of 10. The decimal must be greater than or equal to 1 and less
than 10. For example, in scientific notation:

$$425 = 4.25 \cdot 100 = 4.25 \cdot 10^2$$
$$0.0015 = 1.5 \cdot 0.001 = 1.5 \cdot 10^{-3}.$$

Name _____ Date _____

Study Guide: Practice & Application Exercises
For use with Section 1

Exploration 1

Write each number in words and as a fraction or a mixed number.

1. 0.027　　　　**2.** 15.551　　　　**3.** 23.1099　　　　**4.** 18.3

5. 0.89　　　　**6.** 1.000133　　　　**7.** 42.7　　　　**8.** 60.8009

Replace each __?__ with >, <, or =.

9. 0.91 __?__ 0.95　　　　**10.** 3.2 __?__ 3.02　　　　**11.** 15.988 __?__ 13.999

12. 0.901 __?__ 0.0913　　　　**13.** 14.9 __?__ 1.49　　　　**14.** 7.812 __?__ 7.8120

Exploration 2

Write each power of ten in standard form.

15. 10^{-5}　　　　**16.** 10^0　　　　**17.** 10^4　　　　**18.** 10^{-2}　　　　**19.** 10^{10}

Write each power as a fraction with its denominator in standard form.

20. 5^{-3}　　　　**21.** 7^{-1}　　　　**22.** 2^{-6}　　　　**23.** 3^{-5}　　　　**24.** 4^{-2}

Write each power as a fraction with its denominator in exponential form.

25. 5^{-8}　　　　**26.** 7^{-3}　　　　**27.** 14^{-2}　　　　**28.** 10^{-4}　　　　**29.** 6^{-6}

Exploration 3

Write each product in standard form.

30. $2.7 \cdot 10^5$　　　　**31.** $25.19 \cdot 10^{-4}$　　　　**32.** $99 \cdot 0.0001$

33. $3610 \cdot 10^{-2}$　　　　**34.** $4.5 \cdot 0.00001$　　　　**35.** $12.768 \cdot 10^3$

Write each number in scientific notation.

36. 4512　　　　**37.** 0.0305　　　　**38.** 56,983　　　　**39.** 56.9

40. 0.009　　　　**41.** 15.205　　　　**42.** 0.1117　　　　**43.** 67,100.6

Name _____   Date _____

Quick Quiz
For use after Section 1

1. Write 2.034 as a fraction or a mixed number.

2. Which is greater, 2.39 or 2.389? Explain.

3. Write $7.02 \cdot 10^4$ in standard form.

4. Write 5^{-3} as a fraction with its denominator

   a. in exponential form.   b. in standard form.

5. The farthest distance from Earth to the sun is about 94,500,000 miles. Express that number in scientific notation.

6. Write each product in standard form.

   a. $8.3 \cdot 10^{-4}$ b. $7.045 \cdot 10^2$

7. What is the value of 9^0?

Warm-Up Exercises

For use with Section 2

Evaluate each expression when *a* = 3 and *b* = 6.

1. $a + 2b$

2. $a^2 - b$

3. $5a + ab + 4b$

Simplify each fraction.

4. $\dfrac{8}{24}$

5. $\dfrac{9}{15}$

6. $\dfrac{6}{6}$

ANSWERS

1. 15   2. 3   3. 57   4. $\dfrac{1}{3}$ 5. $\dfrac{3}{5}$ 6. 1

MODULE 2   LABSHEET **2A**

Changing the Horizontal Scale (Use with Question 20 on page 103.)

Directions Use the data in the table to complete parts (a)–(c).

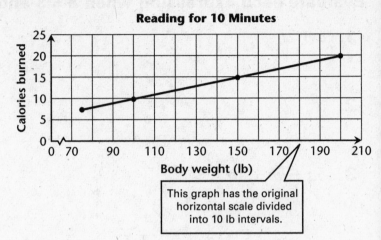

Reading for 10 minutes	
Body Weight (lb)	Calories burned
75	7.35
100	9.8
150	14.7
200	19.6

Reading for 10 Minutes

This graph has the original horizontal scale divided into 10 lb intervals.

a. Write the new scale on the horizontal axis of each graph.

b. Plot the data in the table above on each graph.

c. Connect the points on each graph.

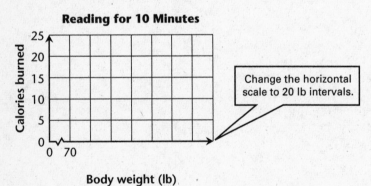

Reading for 10 Minutes

Change the horizontal scale to 20 lb intervals.

Body weight (lb)

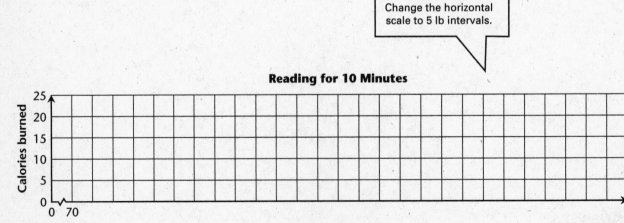

Change the horizontal scale to 5 lb intervals.

Reading for 10 Minutes

Body weight (lb)

Math Thematics, Book 2
Teacher's Resource Book, Modules 1 and 2

Name _____ Date _____

MODULE 2 Practice and Applications
For use with Section 2

For use with Exploration 1

1. Refer to the information below.

A banana has about 107 Calories, while an apple has about 55 Calories.

  a. Write the ratio of the number of Calories in a banana to the number of Calories in an apple in three ways.

  b. About how many times as many Calories are in a banana as in an apple?

2. During exercise, maximum target heart rate can be found using the linear function $t = 0.85m$, where t is a person's maximum target heart rate and m is a person's maximum heart rate.

  a. Make a table of values for the maximum target heart rate for maximum heart rates of 170, 180, 190, and 200 beats per minute.

  b. Plot the data points and connect them.

  c. Maximum heart rate can be found using the formula $m = 220 - a$, where m is a person's maximum heart rate and a is a person's age. Find the maximum heart rate of a 13-year-old student. Then estimate this student's target heart rate.

3. Find the slope of each line.

a.
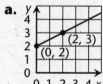

b.

c.
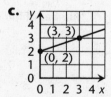

d.
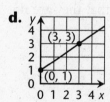

(continued)

Name _____ Date _____

Practice and Applications

For use with Section 2

4. Find the slope of a line with each rise and run.

a. rise 8   **b.** rise 6   **c.** rise 3
   run 4   run 2   run 4

d. rise 5   **e.** rise 3   **f.** rise 2
   run 5   run 1   run 5

g. rise 3   **h.** rise 6   **i.** rise 4
   run 9   run 12   run 5

For use with Exploration 2

5. Rachel ran the 200-meter dash for her school's track team. Refer to the graph shown at the right.

a. A horizontal line segment connects the points for Weeks 2 and 3. What does this show about Rachel's performance during those weeks?

b. What does the graph show about Rachel's performance over the course of the season?

c. How could the graph be changed to better display the data? Explain.

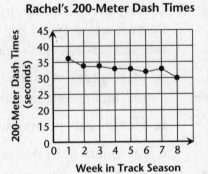

Rachel's 200-Meter Dash Times

6. Refer to the graphs shown at the right.

a. About how many words per minute can Clark type?

b. About how many words per minute can Jenny type?

c. Are these graphs misleading? If they are, explain why and redraw them so that they are not misleading.

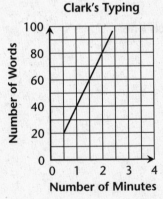
Clark's Typing

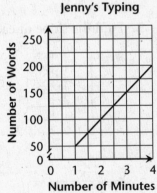
Jenny's Typing

Name _____   Date _____

Study Guide
For use with Section 2

Fuel for Your Body   Interpreting Graphs

GOAL   **LEARN HOW TO:** • choose a scale for a graph
• use formulas to find values and make graphs
• find the slope of a line
• determine how the scale affects the appearance of a graph
• decide when a line graph is appropriate

AS YOU: • investigate the number of Calories burned during exercise
• identify misleading graphs

Exploration 1: Formulas and Graphs

Creating a Ratio

A **ratio** is a comparison of two quantities by division. The ratio of the quantity a to the quantity b can be written in three ways.

$$a \text{ to } b \qquad a : b \qquad \frac{a}{b}$$

Choosing a Scale for a Graph

The numbers written along the axis of a graph are its **scale**. Usually, the *maximum* and the *minimum data values* determine the *range* of the scale. The size of the *interval* depends on how spread out the data values are. The two axes can have different scales and intervals.

Graphing a Linear Function

A **linear function** is a function whose graph is a line or part of a line. The graph below shows the linear function $y = 2x$.

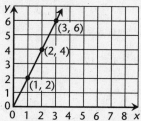

Finding the Slope of a Line

The **slope** of a line is the ratio of the *rise* to the *run*.

The **rise** is the number of units the graph rises between two points.

$$\text{slope} = \frac{\text{rise}}{\text{run}}$$

The **run** is the number of units left or right between the same two points.

Study Guide

For use with Section 2

Example

Find the slope of the line on the graph.

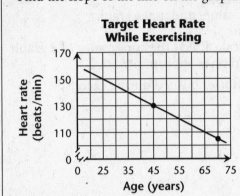

Sample Response

At age 70 the target heart rate while exercising is about 105 beats per minute.

At age 45 the target heart rate while exercising is about 130 beats per minute.

$$\text{slope} = \frac{130 - 105}{45 - 70} \quad \leftarrow \text{rise} \atop \leftarrow \text{run}$$

$$= \frac{25}{-25} = -1$$

Exploration 2: Misleading Graphs

Reading Line Graphs

In a **line graph**, the points representing the data are connected with line segments. Line graphs, such as the one at the right, can be used to show change in data over time.

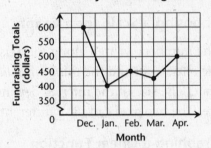

Interpreting Scales

The scales chosen for a graph will affect the way the data appears.

Example

The graphs below show how the data in the table appear different when the scales on the vertical axes are different.

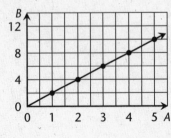

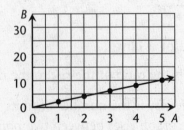

Study Guide: Practice & Application Exercises
For use with Section 2

Exploration 1

Write each ratio in two other ways.

1. $3:4$ **2.** 91 to 34 **3.** $\frac{27}{100}$ **4.** 9 to 1

Use the information below for Exercises 5–7.

An average person blinks 15 times in 1 minute. The number of times b a person blinks in m minutes can be described by the formula $b = 15m$.

5. Make a table of values for the number of times the average person blinks in 10, 20, 30, and 40 minutes.

6. Plot and connect the data points in Exercise 5.

7. Estimate the number of times the average person blinks in 25 minutes.

Find the slope of a line with each rise and run.

8. rise 4 **9.** rise 8 **10.** rise 27 **11.** rise 48 **12.** rise 9
run 8   run 24   run 9   run 6   run 15

Exploration 2

Use the table at the right for Exercises 13–16.

13. Make a line graph for the data in the table.

14. Describe how the daily high and low temperatures change in Madrid, Spain, throughout the year.

15. Describe how the difference between the daily high and low temperatures changes throughout the year.

Average Daily Temperatures (°F) Madrid, Spain		
Month	**High**	**Low**
January	50	34
April	63	43
July	89	61
October	67	48

16. What decision might someone using this graph be trying to make?

Use the table at the right for Exercises 17 and 18.

17. Make two graphs of the data using different scales on the vertical axes.

18. Explain which graph you would show your employer to help you get a pay raise.

Hourly pay	Month
$5.00	January
$5.15	May
$5.20	September

Name _____   Date _____

Quick Quiz

For use after Section 2

1. The number of Calories burned in 15 min of downhill skiing can be described by $C = 0.45b$, where C is the number of Calories burned and b is the body weight in pounds. Complete the table for the number of Calories burned by people weighing 100 lb, 125 lb, 150 lb, and 175 lb in 15 min of downhill skiing.

Calories Burned in 15 Minutes of Downhill Skiing	
Body Weight (lb)	Calories Burned

2. If you were to graph the data from your table, the graph would show a linear function. Why?

3. Find the slope of this line.

4. Find the slope of a line with rise 3 and run 9.

Name _____ Date _____

Mid-Module Quiz
For use after Section 2

1. Write the numbers 0.234, 1.35, 1.336, 0.7 in order from least to greatest.

Write each number in standard form.

2. 3^{-4}

3. $6.278 \cdot 10^6$

Write each number in scientific notation.

4. 64,000

5. 0.00035

6. The monthly cost for using a certain Internet plan can be described by $C = \$10 + \$0.15m$, where C is the cost in dollars and m is the number of minutes in use. Make a table for the monthly cost when 0, 25, 80, and 150 minutes are used in one month.

7. If you were to graph the data from your table, the graph would show a linear function. Why?

8. Find the slope of a line with rise 6 and run 3.

9. Use graph paper to graph the data twice with different vertical or horizontal scales. Make one graph appear to show that T-shirt sales have decreased and label the other graph to show that T-shirt sales are still very popular. Include titles and axes labels for your graph.

Year	Estimated number of school T-shirts sold
1990	1280
1995	1116
2001	1001
2004	920

Solution Guide: Textbook E²

For use with E² on textbook page 112

The Painted Cube

There is only one answer to this problem, but expect the representations to vary. Students may build the cube, draw a picture, use base plans, or in some other way represent the colored cube. All of the *Math Thematics Assessment Scales* should be used to assess student work.

The sample response below shows part of a student's solution.

Partial Solution

I drew a picture of the large cube to get a better idea about which faces were painted. I needed to see inside the large cube so I also drew the three layers of the cube.

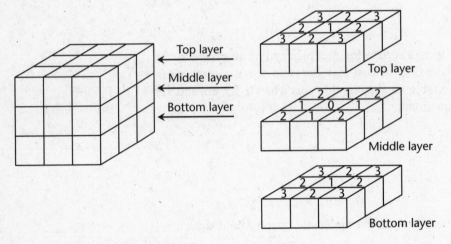

The numbers in the drawings tell how many faces on each small cube are painted. I organized my results in a table.

Number of painted faces	6	5	4	3	2	1	0
Number of small cubes	0	0	0	8	12	6	1

I wondered if it was possible to get 4, 5, or 6 painted faces. I looked at other cubes. My results are below.

Dimensions of large cube	Total number of small cubes	\multicolumn{7}{c}{Number of painted faces on small cubes}
		6	5	4	3	2	1	0
$1 \times 1 \times 1$	1	1	0	0	0	0	0	0
$2 \times 2 \times 2$	8	0	0	0	8	0	0	0
$3 \times 3 \times 3$	27	0	0	0	8	12	6	1
$4 \times 4 \times 4$	64	0	0	0	8	24	24	8
$5 \times 5 \times 5$	125	0	0	0	8	36	54	27
$n \times n \times n, n \geq 2$	$n \cdot n \cdot n$	0	0	0	8	$12 \cdot (n-2)$	$6 \cdot (n-2) \cdot (n-2)$	$(n-2) \cdot (n-2) \cdot (n-2)$

I found a general rule for finding the number of painted faces if the dimensions of the cube are greater than or equal to 2. I also realized that you could never paint 4 or 5 faces no matter what the size of your large cube.

Name _____   Date _____

Alternate E²
For use with Module 2

A Calendar Problem

The Situation
Take the calendar page for any month of the year and choose any 3 by 3 array of dates on it as shown below. What is the sum of the numbers in the array?

January						
Sun.	Mon.	Tues.	Wed.	Thurs.	Fri.	Sat.
				1	2	3
4	5	6	7	8	9	10
11	12	13	14	15	16	17
18	19	20	21	22	23	24
25	26	27	28	29	30	31

The Problem
How is the sum of the numbers in any 3 by 3 array on a month of a calendar page related to the middle number in the array?

Something to Think About
- How is each number in a calendar related to the number in the row above it?
- How is each number in a calendar related to the number to its left?

Present Your Results
Tell how the sum of the numbers in any 3 by 3 array on the calendar page for any month is related to the middle number in the array. Explain how you know this is always true.

Solution Guide: Alternate E²
For use with Module 2

A Calendar Problem

There is only one solution to this problem, but students' approaches and reasoning will vary. All of the *Math Thematics Assessment Scales* can be used to assess students' solutions, but the problem does not provide much opportunity to use mathematical terms, so you may not want to score students on the Mathematical Language Scale.

Each sample response below shows part of a student's solution.

Partial Solution

I tried several 3 by 3 arrays on different pages of a calendar, and in every one of them the sum of the numbers in the array was 9 times the middle number. I decided this must always be true, but I wasn't sure why. After studying the example for a while, it hit me.

Pick a number on a calendar page. The number to its left is one less than the number and the number to its right is one more than the number so the three numbers must add up to 3 times the number you started with. In the example:

$$12 + 13 + 14 = (13 - 1) + 13 + (13 + 1)$$
$$= 13 + 13 + 13 - 1 + 1$$
$$= 3 \cdot 13$$

Also, each number in the top row of the array is 7 less than the number below it, and each number in the bottom row is 7 more than the number above it. So the sum of the numbers in the top row is 21 less than the sum of the numbers in the middle row and the sum of the numbers in the bottom row is 21 more. In the example:

$$5 + 6 + 7 = (12 - 7) + (13 - 7) + (14 - 7) \quad \text{and} \quad 19 + 20 + 21 = (12 + 7) + (13 + 7) + (14 + 7)$$
$$= (12 + 13 + 14) - 7 - 7 - 7 \qquad\qquad\qquad = (12 + 13 + 14) + 7 + 7 + 7$$
$$= (12 + 13 + 14) - 21 \qquad\qquad\qquad\qquad = (12 + 13 + 14) + 21$$

That means that if you add the numbers in the top row and the numbers in the bottom row, the sum will be twice the sum of the numbers in the middle row. When you add the numbers in the middle row to the sum, the result is 3 times the sum of the numbers in the middle row or 3 times 3 times the middle number or 9 times the middle number.

Partial Solution

The numbers in a 3 by 3 array on a calendar page are related as shown below.

$n - 8$	$n - 7$	$n - 6$
$n - 1$	n	$n + 1$
$n + 6$	$n + 7$	$n + 8$

Sum $= (n + 8) + (n + 7) + (n + 6) + (n + 1) + n + (n - 8) + (n - 7) + (n - 6) + (n - 1)$
$= (n + n + n + n + n + n + n + n + n) + (8 + 7 + 6 + 1) - (8 + 7 + 6 + 1)$
$= 9n + 0$
$= 9n$

So the sum of the numbers in the array will always be 9 times the middle number.

Other Considerations

- Students may also extend the solution to 5 by 5 arrays, 7 by 7 arrays, etc.

Warm-Up Exercises

For use with Section 3

Write the next three numbers.

1. 5, 15, 25, 35, ...

2. 300, 298, 296, 294, ...

3. 2, 22, 222, 2222, ...

4. 1, 3, 2, 4, 3, 5, 4, 6, ...

ANSWERS

1. 45, 55, 65   2. 292, 290, 288   3. 22,222; 222,222; 2,222,222   4. 5, 7, 6

Name _____ Date _____

Equations (Use with Question 13 on page 120.)

Directions For each equation:

- Complete the table of values.
- Graph the points on the coordinate plane.

$t = 2n + 6$

Term Number n	Number of Squares t
1	
2	
3	
4	14
5	
6	

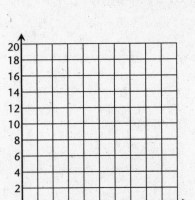

$t = 2(n + 3)$

Term Number n	Number of Squares t
1	
2	
3	
4	14
5	
6	

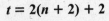

$t = 2(n + 2) + 2$

Term Number n	Number of Squares t
1	
2	
3	
4	14
5	
6	

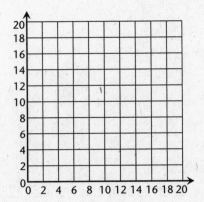

Name _____   Date _____

Practice and Applications

For use with Section 3

For use with Exploration 1

Use the table for Exercises 1–3.

Term number	1	2	3	4	5	6	...	10	...	90
Shape sequence					?	?	?	...	?	...
Number sequence	2	4	6	8	?	?	...	?	...	?

1. How are the number sequence and the shape sequence related?

2. **a.** Draw a picture to model the 5th term of the shape sequence.

   b. What is the 5th term of the number sequence?

3. **a.** What pattern can you use to predict the 6th term of the shape sequence?

   b. Predict what the 6th term of the number sequence will be.

   c. Predict the 10th and 90th terms of the number sequence.

4. Write an equation for each word sentence. Use *t* for the term and *n* for the term number.

   a. The term is seven times the term number.

   b. The term is two less than the term number.

   c. The term is six more than the term number.

   d. The term is one fourth the term number.

5. For each sequence, make a table, draw a graph, and write an equation. Then predict the 10th term.

   a. 6, 12, 18, 24, ...

   b. 28, 26, 24, 22, ...

(continued)

MODULE 2 Practice and Applications
For use with Section 3

For use with Exploration 2

6. Use the distributive property to rewrite each expression.

a. $5(40 + 7)$

b. $8(2x + 16)$

c. $72 + 81$

d. $3x - 15$

e. $4x + 16x$

f. $x(14 - 9)$

7. Use the commutative, associative, and distributive properties to show that the equations are equivalent.

a. $d = 5(c + 8)$; $d = 5c + 40$

b. $t = x(5 + 7) - 7$; $t = 12x - 7$

c. $w = 4(2z - 1) + 2$; $w = 2(4z - 1)$

d. $x = (y - 3) + 2y$; $x = 3(y - 1)$

8. A student tried to use the commutative, associative, and distributive properties to rewrite each expression. In each case, the student used the properties incorrectly. Explain the student's errors. Then rewrite each expression to make it true.

a. $3(2x + 8) = 3x + 24$

b. $7(7t + 7) = 49t + 7$

c. $5(n + 5) = 30n$

d. $6(y + 2) + 3 = 6y + 30$

9. Rebekah is buying 2 pounds of apples and 3 pounds of peaches at the farmer's market. Both types of fruit are on sale for 75¢ per pound.

a. Use the distributive property to write two expressions for the amount Rebekah paid for the fruit.

b. How much did Rebekah pay for the fruit?

c. Which expression from part (a) did you use to find the cost of the fruit? Why did you use this expression?

Name _____ Date _____

Study Guide
For use with Section 3

Halley and His Comet   Sequences and Equivalent Equations

GOAL **LEARN HOW TO:** • use tables, graphs, and equations to model sequences
• make predictions
• use the associative, commutative, and distributive properties to simplify expressions

AS YOU: • explore patterns
• investigate equivalent equations

Exploration 1: Modeling Sequences

Sequences

A **sequence** is an ordered list of numbers or objects called **terms**. The **term number** tells the position of each term in the sequence.

You can use the pattern of a sequence to predict a specific term of the sequence.

2, 4, 6, 8, 10, … is a sequence.

The *1st term* of the sequence above is 2.
The *5th term* of the sequence above is 10.

Each term in the sequence is twice its term number. So, the 6th term is 12.

Using Tables and Graphs

You can use a table of values and a graph to explore a sequence and predict future terms.

> **Example**
>
> The values in the table are plotted on the graph shown at the right. By continuing the pattern made by the points, you can predict future terms. For example, the 6th term is 18.
>
> | Term Number | Term |
> |:-----------:|:----:|
> | 1 | 3 |
> | 2 | 6 |
> | 3 | 9 |
>
>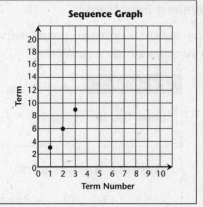

Using Equations

You can use variables to write an equation that shows how each term in a sequence is related to its term number. Let n = the term number and let t = the term. Then,

$t = 3 \cdot n$ or $t = 3n$

models the sequence shown above.

Name _____ Date _____

 **Study Guide**
For use with Section 3

Exploration 2: Equivalent Equations

Distributive Properties

The **distributive property of multiplication over addition** says that for any numbers a, b, and c:

$$a(b + c) = ab + ac \quad \text{and} \quad (b + c)a = ba + ca$$

The **distributive property of multiplication over subtraction** says that for any numbers a, b, and c:

$$a(b - c) = ab - ac \quad \text{and} \quad (b - c)a = ba - ca$$

You can use the distributive properties to simplify and rewrite expressions.

Example

Use the distributive properties to rewrite each expression.

a. $4(2x + 9)$ **b.** $64x + 88$ **c.** $3x + 15x$

Sample Response

a. $4(2x + 9) = 4(2x) + 4(9) = 8x + 36$

b. $64x + 88 = 8(8x) + 8(11) = 8(8x + 11)$

c. $3x + 15x = 3x(1) + 3x(5) = 3x(1 + 5)$

Equivalent Equations

You can use the distributive, commutative, and associative properties to show that two equations are equivalent.

Example

Show that the equation $y = 2(2x + 9) + 10$ is equivalent to $y = 4(x + 7)$.

Sample Response

$y = 2(2x + 9) + 10$ ← Rewrite the original equation.

$y = 4x + 18 + 10$ ← Use the distributive property.

$y = 4x + (18 + 10)$ ← Use the associative property.

$y = 4x + 28$ ← Simplify.

$y = 4(x + 7)$ ← Use the distributive property.

Name _____ Date _____

Study Guide: Practice & Application Exercises

For use with Section 3

Exploration 1

For Exercises 1–3, write an equation for each word sentence.
Use *t* for the term and *n* for the term number.

1. The term is four times the term number.

2. The term is two less than the term number.

3. The term is six more than twice the term number.

4. Make a table, draw a graph, and write an equation for the sequence
   6, 12, 18, 24, … . Then predict the 100th term.

5. **Visual Thinking** Sketch the 6th shape in the sequence below.

Exploration 2

Use the distributive property to rewrite each expression.

6. $7p - 35$ 7. $10(9) + 9$ 8. $17x + 6x$ 9. $(61 - 8)7$

**Use the distributive property and mental math to find each
product. Show how you did each computation.**

10. $36 \cdot 48$ 11. $14 \cdot 112$ 12. $30 \cdot 120$

**Use the distributive property to evaluate each expression
mentally.**

13. $3(3.4) + 3(5.6)$ 14. $5(5.7) - 5(2.7)$ 15. $8(6.2) + 8(3.8)$

16. Emma's rectangular bedroom floor is 16 feet long and 11 feet wide.
    The height of her ceiling is 8 feet. Emma wants to put wallpaper on
    her walls.

    a. Write two equivalent equations that Emma can use to find
       the total area of her bedroom walls. (Hint: Draw a diagram to
       determine the dimensions of each wall.)

    b. The wallpaper costs $3.75 per square foot. How much money will
       it cost Emma to buy wallpaper for her room?

    c. Which equation from part (a) did you use to find the cost in
       part (b)? Show that your other equation from part (a) will give
       the same price.

Name _____   Date _____

Quick Quiz
For use after Section 3

1. Write an equation for the following word sentence, using *t* for the term and *n* for the term number: *The term is two more than five times the term number.*

    Equation: _____

2. For the following sequence: 5, 11, 17, 23, ...

    a. Complete the table.

Term Number	1	2	3	4	5	6
Term	5	11	17	23		

    b. Graph the points on a coordinate plane.

    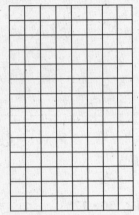

    c. Write an equation. Use *t* for term and *n* for term number.

    d. Predict the 200th term.

3. Use the distributive property to rewrite each expression.

    a. $5(m + 11)$ **b.** $4x - 12$

4. Use the commutative, associative, and distributive properties to show that the equations are equivalent.

    $$y = 3(x - 7) + 2x \qquad y = 5x - 21$$

Name _____ Date _____

Warm-Up Exercises
For use with Section 4

Tell which problem solving strategy or strategies you would use to solve each problem.

1. finding a path through a maze

2. deciding in what order you should deliver packages that are to be delivered to different locations

3. trying to find your lost keys

4. deciding how you can rearrange the furniture in your room

ANSWERS

Sample Responses: 1. work backwards   2. make an organized list, make a diagram

3. act it out (retrace your steps) and use logical reasoning   4. draw a diagram

MODULE 2

Last Card Table (Use with Questions 19 and 20 on page 136 and Exercise 14 on page 141.)

Directions Use the table below and follow the directions in Questions 19 and 20 to extend your solution to the *Last Card Problem*.

Number of Cards	1	2	3	4	5	6	7	8	9	10	11	12	13	14	15	16	17	18	19	20
Number on last card	1	2	2	4	2	4	6	8	2	4	6	8	10	12	14					

Number of Cards	21	22	23	24	25	26	27	28	29	30	31	32	33
Number on last card													

Two Assessment Scales (Use with Questions 22 and 23 on page 136.)

Directions Use a marker to draw a segment along each scale to the point that describes your group's work for Question 9 on page 132.

▬▬ *If your score is in the shaded area, explain why on the back of this sheet and stop.*   ☆ *The star indicates that you excelled in some way.*

 Problem Solving

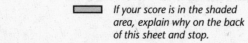 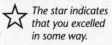

❶   **❷**   **❸**   **❹**   **❺**

I did not understand the problem well enough to get started or I did not show any work.

I understood the problem well enough to make a plan and to work toward a solution.

I made a plan, I used it to solve the problem, and I verified my solution.

 Connections

❶   **❷**   **❸**   **❹**   **❺**

I attempted or solved the problem and then stopped.

I found patterns and used them to extend the solution to other cases, or I recognized that this problem relates to other problems, mathematical ideas, or applications.

I extended the ideas in the solution to the general case, or I showed how this problem relates to other problems, mathematical ideas, or applications.

Name _____ Date _____

Problem Solving Scales (Use with Exercise 11 on page 140.)

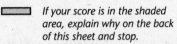 If your score is in the shaded area, explain why on the back of this sheet and stop. 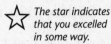 The star indicates that you excelled in some way.

 Problem Solving

❶   **❷**   **❸**   **❹**   **❺**

I did not understand the problem well enough to get started or I did not show any work.

I understood the problem well enough to make a plan and to work toward a solution.

I made a plan, I used it to solve the problem, and I verified my solution.

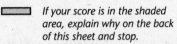 If your score is in the shaded area, explain why on the back of this sheet and stop. 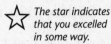 The star indicates that you excelled in some way.

Problem Solving

❶   **❷**   **❸**   **❹**   **❺**

I did not understand the problem well enough to get started or I did not show any work.

I understood the problem well enough to make a plan and to work toward a solution.

I made a plan, I used it to solve the problem, and I verified my solution.

Problem Solving and Connections Scales (Use with Exercise 13 on page 141.)

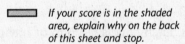 If your score is in the shaded area, explain why on the back of this sheet and stop. 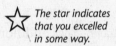 The star indicates that you excelled in some way.

Problem Solving

❶   **❷**   **❸**   **❹**   **❺**

I did not understand the problem well enough to get started or I did not show any work.

I understood the problem well enough to make a plan and to work toward a solution.

I made a plan, I used it to solve the problem, and I verified my solution.

 Connections

❶   **❷**   **❸**   **❹**   **❺**

I attempted or solved the problem and then stopped.

I found patterns and used them to extend the solution to other cases, or I recognized that this problem relates to other problems, mathematical ideas, or applications.

I extended the ideas in the solution to the general case, or I showed how this problem relates to other problems, mathematical ideas, or applications.

Name _____ Date _____

Practice and Applications
For use with Section 4

For use with Exploration 1

1. Assume a person bicycling 1 mi at a rate of 10 mi/hr will burn 80 Cal.

   a. At this rate, how many minutes does it take to cycle 1 mi?

   b. At this rate, how many minutes per week must a person bicycle to burn 2000 Cal?

2. Denise earns $7.00 per hour plus $2.00 for every sale she makes. If Denise earned $239 for 25 hours of work last week, how many sales did she make?

For use with Exploration 2

3. Four equilateral triangles can be placed side by side as shown to form a parallelogram with a perimeter of 6 in. If another parallelogram is formed the same way using 30 triangles, what will its perimeter be?

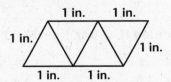

4. A farmer has 8 cows and horses. Each cow is fed 6 lb of hay per meal and each horse is fed 8 lb. It takes 52 lb of hay to feed all 8 animals one meal. How many horses are there?

5. Derrick's scores on his first three science tests are 88, 86, and 87. What score must he get on his fourth test to raise his average to 90?

6. Renzo needs $600 to buy some speakers. The table shows how much money he had in March, April, and May. If this pattern continues, in what month will he be able to buy the speakers?

Month	Amount of money
March	$90
April	$165
May	$240

7. Peter Pan Preschool has a phone relay to inform parents if the preschool is closed during bad weather. The director calls three parents who each call four other parents. These four parents then each call three other parents who each call two more parents. How many parents are called in all?

(continued)

Name _____   Date _____

Practice and Applications
For use with Section 4

8. The chess club has enough money to buy 8 boards or 64 chess pieces. The members decide to buy 32 chess pieces. How many boards can they buy?

9. Jared wanted to find the total number of squares in the diagram shown at the right.

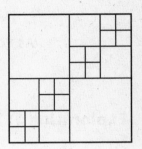

   a. Jared decided to solve the problem above by first counting the number of small squares. Then he planned on counting the larger squares. He counted 27 total squares and recorded 27 as his answer. How would you score Jared's work on the problem solving scale? Why?

   b. Solve the problem. Is your solution the same as Jared's?

   c. What score would you give your solution in part (b) on the problem solving scale?

10. **a.** Suppose you have quarters, dimes, and pennies with a total value of $1.08. How many of each coin can you have without being able to make change for a dollar?

   b. What score would you give your work in part (a) on the problem solving scale?

For use with Exploration 3

11. **a.** Suppose Julia has $15. She wants to buy at least one of each type of book at the book sale and she wants to use as much of $15 as possible to buy some gifts. How many of each type of book should Julia buy?

   b. What score would you give your solution in part (a) on the problem solving and connections scale?

Book Sale	
Mysteries	$1.95
Novel	$2.35
Science	$2.65
Fantasy	$1.45
Nature	$2.95

Name _____ Date _____

 **Study Guide**
For use with Section 4

Young Problem Solvers   Problem Solving and Connections

GOAL   **LEARN HOW TO:** • recognize the steps of the 4-step approach to problem solving
• apply the 4-step approach to problem solving
• use the Problem Solving Scale
• use the Connections Scale

AS YOU: • solve a problem similar to the *Two Jar Puzzle*
• predict outcomes in the *Last Card Problem*
• find ways to extend your solution to the *Last Card Problem*

Exploration 1: Four Steps to Problem Solving

Step 1: Understand the Problem

• **Read** the **problem** carefully, probably several times.

• **Identify** what the **question** is.

• **Restate** the **problem** in your own words.

• **Identify** the **information needed** to solve the problem, and determine if any of it is missing.

Step 2: Make a Plan

You may have to choose several problem solving strategies such as:

• try a simpler problem
• make an organized list
• act it out
• use logical reasoning
• make a picture or diagram

• make a table
• look for a pattern
• guess and check
• work backward
• use an equation

Step 3: Carry Out the Plan

• Solve the problem using the strategies you selected.

• You may need to change strategies.

Step 4: Look Back

• Check that you answered the question being asked.

• Check that your solution seems reasonable.

• Check that your work is accurate.

• Try to find another method to solve the problem and compare the results.

• Study the solution to see if the method can be generalized or extended to other situations or to solve other problems.

Math Thematics, Book 2
2-42 Teacher's Resource Book, Modules 1 and 2

Study Guide
For use with Section 4

Example

A phone call costs $0.35 for the first minute and $0.12 for each minute thereafter. Jordan's bill for calling her brother was $1.31. How many minutes did she talk?

▤ Sample Response ▤

Step 1:
- Read the problem carefully.
- Identify the question.
- Restate the problem in your own words.
- Identify the necessary information.

How many minutes did she talk?
first minute = $0.35;
each additional minute = $0.12;
Her bill was $1.31.

Step 2:
- Choose a strategy.

Since I know how much the bill was, I will *work backward* to solve.

Step 3:
- Solve the problem.

Subtract the charge for the first minute from the total. Divide by 12 to find the number of additional minutes.

$$\begin{array}{r} \$1.31 \\ -\ 0.35 \\ \hline \$0.96 \end{array} \qquad \begin{array}{r} 8 \\ 12\overline{)96} \\ \underline{96} \\ 0 \end{array} \qquad \begin{array}{r} 8 \\ +\ 1 \\ \hline 9 \end{array}$$

The phone call lasted 9 min.

Step 4:
- Check that you answered the question.
- Check that your answer seems reasonable.
- Check that your work is accurate.

Check:
$0.35 + 8 \cdot \$0.12 = \$0.35 + \$0.96$
$= \$1.31$ ✔

Study Guide
For use with Section 4

Exploration 2: The Last Card Problem

Once you have solved a problem, you can use the pattern or model that you used to solve it to make predictions. For instance, in the Example above, you could predict the cost of a 30 min call by using the model $0.35 + 29 \cdot $0.12 = $3.83.

Problem Solving Scale

This problem solving scale is used to assess how well you apply the 4-step approach to problem solving.

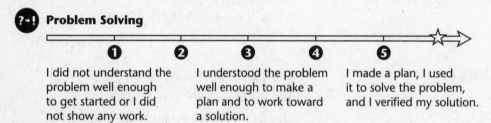

?→! **Problem Solving**

❶ I did not understand the problem well enough to get started or I did not show any work.

❷

❸ I understood the problem well enough to make a plan and to work toward a solution.

❹

❺ I made a plan, I used it to solve the problem, and I verified my solution.

When you assess your work using the problem solving scale, think about whether you:

• understood the problem

• made a plan

• carried out the plan to solve the problem

• looked back to verify your solution

Example

Suppose you were asked to find the next number in the pattern 1, 4, 7, 10, ...

To solve the problem, you used a dot pattern to represent the numbers. You determined the answer was 13. What score would you rate on the problem solving scale?

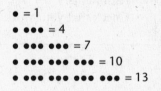

• = 1

• ••• = 4

• ••• ••• = 7

• ••• ••• ••• = 10

• ••• ••• ••• ••• = 13

Sample Response

You would probably rate this solution a **4** on the problem solving scale because you made a plan, used it to solve the problem, but did not verify your solution.

Math Thematics, Book 2
2-44 Teacher's Resource Book, Modules 1 and 2

Name _____ Date _____

Study Guide
For use with Section 4

Exploration 3: Making Connections

Connections Scale

You can use the connections scale to assess how well you make connections to other problems, mathematical concepts, or applications.

 Connections

① — **②** — **③** — **④** — **⑤**

① I attempted or solved the problem and then stopped.

③ I found patterns and used them to extend the solution to other cases, or I recognized that this problem relates to other problems, mathematical ideas, or applications.

⑤ I extended the ideas in the solution to the general case, or I showed how this problem relates to other problems, mathematical ideas, or applications.

You might score a **3** on the connections scale if you:

• recognize how the problem is related to other problems

• recognize connections to other mathematical topics

• extend the solution

You might score a **5** on the connections scale if you:

• show how the problem or mathematics can be applied elsewhere

• extend the problem to the general case

Example

Refer back to the problem in the previous Example.

Suppose you used a dot pattern to represent the numbers as shown below, indicating the position of each number in the pattern. You then wrote a formula for finding any number in the pattern, and used it to determine that the next number is 13. What score would you rate on the connections scale?

1st ● = 1
2nd ● ●●● = 4
3rd ● ●●● ●●● = 7
4th ● ●●● ●●● ●●● = 10
5th ● ●●● ●●● ●●● ●●● = 13

Let t = the term number.
Then $1 + 3(t - 1)$ = the number in the tth position.

Find the number in the 5th position.

$1 + 3(t - 1) = 1 + 3(5 - 1) \leftarrow t = 5$
$\qquad\qquad = 1 + 3(4) = 1 + 12 = 13$

The next number in the pattern is 13.

■ Sample Response ■

You would probably rate this solution a **5** on the connections scale because you extended the solution to the general case.

Name _____ Date _____

Study Guide: Practice & Application Exercises

MODULE **2**

For use with Section 4

Exploration 1

Assume a person typing 360 words at the rate of 90 words per minute earns $2.

1. At this rate, how many minutes would it take to type 360 words?

2. At this rate, how many words would a person need to type to earn $30?

3. How many hours would a person need to type to earn $1000?

4. Writing Is getting paid $10 per 1800 words better pay? Explain.

Exploration 2

5. A restaurant has square tables that seat 2 people on each side. If two tables are placed end-to-end, then 12 people may be seated. If 10 tables are placed end-to-end, how many people may be seated?

6. Inga and Dante work at a movie theater taking tickets. They are both working today, but they have different schedules. Inga works every third day and Dante works every other day. How many times will they both be working together on the same day during the next 27 days?

7. Choose the letter of the pattern(s) that can be folded into a square pyramid. Then draw another pattern that will work.

A.

B.

C.
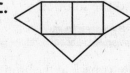

8. Suppose you did not answer Exercise 7. How would you rate your work on the problem solving scale? Why?

9. If you chose the correct letters in Exercise 7 but did not draw another pattern, how would you rate yourself on the problem solving scale? Why?

Exploration 3

10. Find the next number in the number pattern 3, 5, 7, 9, … . Extend your work to find the 200th number in the pattern. Assess your work using the connections scale.

Name _____   Date _____

Quick Quiz
For use after Section 4

1. You have $1000 to spend stocking the school store with T-shirts, sweatshirts, and hats. How could you use a 4-step approach in deciding how to place your order?

2. Give an example of how a student could get a **5** on the problem solving scale and a **1** on the connections scale.

3. Sammie has 3 shirts, 2 pairs of pants, 2 pairs of shoes, and 3 pairs of socks. How many different outfits does she have?

4. **a.** For Question 3, write down the number of choices for each category and the number of different combinations. How are the numbers related?

   b. What do you think the answer to Question 3 would be for a person with 10 shirts, 15 pairs of pants, 8 pairs of shoes, and 20 pairs of socks?

Warm-Up Exercises

For use with Section 5

Complete each pair of equivalent fractions.

1. $\dfrac{3}{8} = \dfrac{?}{32}$

2. $\dfrac{5}{9} = \dfrac{10}{?}$

3. $\dfrac{?}{10} = \dfrac{2}{5}$

4. $\dfrac{12}{24} = \dfrac{1}{?}$

5. $\dfrac{8}{9} = \dfrac{?}{27}$

6. $\dfrac{45}{?} = \dfrac{9}{12}$

ANSWERS

1. 12   2. 18   3. 4   4. 2   5. 24   6. 60

Game Board (Use with the *Setting the Stage* on page 143 and with
Question 12(b)–(c) on page 146.)

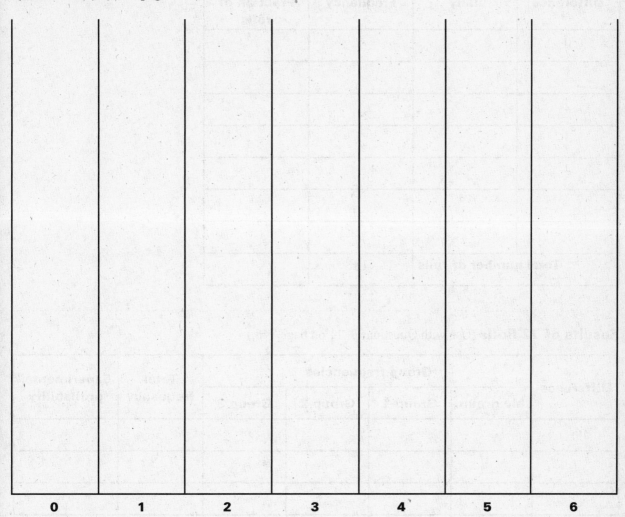

0	1	2	3	4	5	6

Frequency Table (Use with the *Setting the Stage* on page 143 and with
Question 12(e) on page 146.)

Game	Tally of rolls	Total number of rolls
1		
2		
3		

Results of 18 Rolls (Use with Questions 5, 6, 8, 9(a), and 10 on pages 144–146.)

Difference	Tally	Frequency	Fraction of rolls
0			
1			
2			
3			
4			
5			
6			
Total number of rolls		18	

Results of 72 Rolls (Use with Questions 9–11 on page 146.)

Difference	Group frequencies				Total frequency	Experimental probability
	My group	Group 1	Group 2	Group 3		
0						
1						
2						
3						
4						
5						
6						
Total number of rolls					72	

MODULE 2   **LABSHEET** ⬤5C

Rolling One Number Cube (Use with Question 14 on page 147.)

Directions Follow the steps below to complete the table showing the
Results of Rolling One Number Cube.

• Find the theoretical probability of each outcome and record it in the last
  column of the table.

• Find the sum of the theoretical probabilities of the six outcomes and record it
  in the table.

• Take turns rolling a number cube. Keep a tally of the results for 30 rolls.
  Record the frequency of each outcome for your group.

• Record the results from four other groups in the table. Then add the
  frequencies to get a total frequency of each outcome for 150 rolls.

• Find the experimental probability of each outcome based on the frequencies
  for 150 rolls.

Results of Rolling One Number Cube								
Outcome	**Frequencies for 30 rolls**					**Frequency for 150 rolls**	**Probabilities**	
	My group	**Group 1**	**Group 2**	**Group 3**	**Group 4**		**Experimental**	**Theoretical**
1								
2								
3								
4								
5								$\frac{1}{6}$
6								
					Sum of theoretical probabilities			

MODULE 2   **LABSHEET** **5D**

Difference Chart (Use with Questions 17 and 18 on page 148.)

Directions Suppose you roll a red number cube and a blue number cube.
Complete the *Difference Chart* below to show what difference results from
each roll. An example is shown. Then answer the questions below.

Blue Red	1	2	3	4	5	6
1					(5 − 1) 4	
2						
3						
4			(4 − 3) 1			
5						
6						

a. Which difference occurs most often in the chart? Which occurs least often?

b. How many boxes are there to fill in on the chart (including the ones filled in for you)?

c. What fraction of the boxes contain a difference of 4?

d. What is the theoretical probability of rolling a difference of 4?

e. What fraction of the boxes contain a difference of 6?

f. What is the theoretical probability of rolling a difference of 6?

....

Difference Game Theoretical Probability Table
(Use with Questions 18 and 19 on page 148.)

Directions Complete the table at the right by finding the
theoretical probability of each difference shown in the
Difference Chart above. Then find the sum of the
theoretical probabilities.

Theoretical Probabilities for the *Difference Game*
$P(0) =$
$P(1) =$
$P(2) = \dfrac{8}{36}$
$P(3) =$
$P(4) =$
$P(5) =$
$P(6) =$
Sum $=$

Name _____ Date _____

MODULE 2 Practice and Applications
For use with Section 5

For use with Exploration 1

1. Tell whether you think the probability of each event is 0, 1, or somewhere in between. If the probability is in between, do you think it is greater than or less than $\frac{1}{2}$? Give a reason for your answer.

   a. You will visit the zoo this year.

   b. You will go swimming this weekend.

   c. Someone in your household will go to the grocery store this week.

   d. You will hike to the top of a mountain today.

2. Jackie spun the spinner shown at the right 38 times. She got an odd number on 16 spins.

   a. Based on Jackie's results, what is the experimental probability of getting an odd number on a spin?

   b. Describe an event that has a probability of 1 and an event that has a probability of 0.

3. What are all the possible outcomes when you toss a number cube?

4. Toss a coin 30 times. Record your results in a frequency table. Then find the experimental probability of getting heads and the experimental probability of getting tails.

5. Suppose you spin the two spinners shown at the right. List at least 3 outcomes that will produce each event.

   a. a difference of 2

   b. a difference of 0

   c. a sum of 8

   d. an even sum

6. Suppose a bag contains 12 marbles, with 3 each of the colors red, yellow, blue, and green. An experiment involves picking a marble from the bag and putting it back in the bag. The table shows the results after the experiment has been repeated 100 times. Find each experimental probability.

Outcome	Frequency
red	24
yellow	30
blue	26
green	20

   a. P(red)
   b. P(yellow)
   c. P(blue)
   d. P(green)

   e. P(not green)
   f. P(green or yellow)
   g. P(not red)
   h. P(purple)

(continued)

MODULE 2

Practice and Applications
For use with Section 5

For use with Exploration 2

7. Suppose a number cube is rolled once. Find the theoretical probabilities $P(1)$, $P(2)$, and $P(5)$.

8. Suppose you spin the two spinners shown below. Copy and complete the table to show the sums (outcomes) that can occur.

Spinner 1   Spinner 2

	Spinner 1			
Spinner 2	**1**	**2**	**3**	**4**
1				
2				
3				
4				
5				
6				

Find the theoretical probability of each event.

a. $P(2)$ **b.** $P(6)$ **c.** $P(1)$

d. $P(8)$ **e.** $P(3)$ **f.** $P(7)$

g. $P(4 \text{ or } 5)$ **h.** $P(\text{even})$ **i.** $P(12)$

9. Suppose an experiment involves spinning the spinner once.

a. What are all the possible outcomes of the experiment?

b. Are spinning an A and spinning a B equally likely events? Why or why not?

c. What fraction of the spins do you expect to land on A? on B? Give a reason for your answer.

d. Suppose you repeat the experiment 30 times. What results do you expect? Do you think the results will always match your expectations? Why or why not?

10. Sketch a spinner for each situation.

a. The possible outcomes are J and K. The probability of spinning a J is three times the probability of spinning a K.

b. The possible outcomes are A, B, and C. The probability of spinning an A is $\frac{1}{2}$. The probability of spinning a B is $\frac{1}{4}$.

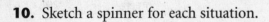

Math Thematics, Book 2
Teacher's Resource Book, Modules 1 and 2

Name _____ Date _____

Study Guide
For use with Section 5

Likely or Unlikely   Probability

GOAL **LEARN HOW TO:** • list the outcomes for an event
• find and compare experimental probabilities
• find theoretical probabilities

AS YOU: • analyze the *Difference Game*
• explore outcomes when rolling one or two number cubes

Exploration 1: What Are the Chances?

Probability and Experimental Probability

A **probability** is a number from 0 through 1 that tells how likely it is
that an event will happen. An **event** is any set of one or more outcomes.

When you roll a number cube or spin a
spinner and record the outcome, you are
conducting an **experiment**. An **outcome**
is the result of an experiment.

Spinning the spinner below is an *experiment*.
There are two possible *outcomes*: A or B.

When a probability is found by repeating
an experiment and recording the results,
the probability is called an **experimental
probability**. The experimental probability
is the ratio of the number of times an
event occurred to the number of times
the experiment was conducted.

Suppose the spinner was spun 8 times and
"B" resulted 3 times. The experimental
probability would be $= \frac{3}{8}$.

Example

A pair of number cubes was rolled 32 times and
the sum was recorded. The results of this experiment are shown in the frequency table at the
right. Use the frequency table to determine the
experimental probability of rolling a sum of 5.

Sum	Frequency
2	1
3	3
4	3
5	**6**
6	4
7	5
8	4
9	4
10	2
11	1
12	0

(continued on next page)

Study Guide
For use with Section 5

■ Sample Response ■

Since a sum of 5 occurred in 6 of the 32 rolls, the experimental probability of a sum of 5 is $\frac{6}{32}$, or $\frac{3}{16}$. This can also be written as $P(\text{sum of 5}) = \frac{3}{16}$.

Exploration 2: Theoretical Probability

A **theoretical probability** is a probability that is determined without actually doing an experiment.

When two or more outcomes have the same chance of occurring, the outcomes are **equally likely**.

Example

Tell whether the outcomes W, X, Y, and Z on each spinner below are equally likely to occur. Then find the theoretical probability of spinning an X.

a.   **b.**

■ Sample Response ■

a. Since the spinner is divided into four equal-sized sectors, the four outcomes (W, X, Y, and Z) are equally likely to occur.

Since the four sectors of the spinner are the same size, the theoretical probability is

$$P(X) = \frac{1}{4}.$$

b. Since the spinner is not divided into four equal-sized sectors, the four outcomes (W, X, Y, and Z) are not equally likely to occur.

The sector labeled "X" appears to be approximately one-eighth of the whole spinner, so the theoretical probability of spinning X is

$$P(X) = \frac{1}{8}.$$

Name _____   Date _____

Study Guide: Practice & Application Exercises
For use with Section 5

Exploration 1

Trisha spun the spinner shown 25 times. She got an odd number 15 times. Use this information for Exercises 1 and 2.

1. Based on Trisha's results, what is the experimental probability of getting an odd number on a spin?

2. Describe an event that has a probability of 1 and an event that has a probability of 0.

3. What are the possible outcomes when you roll a number cube?

4. Toss a coin 30 times. Record your results in a frequency table. Then find the experimental probability of getting heads and the experimental probability of getting tails.

Exploration 2

Suppose you toss two coins. Find the theoretical probability of each event.

5. P(two heads)

6. P(two tails)

7. P(one heads)

8. P(one tails)

For Exercises 9–12, suppose an experiment involves spinning this spinner once.

9. What are all the possible outcomes of the experiment?

10. Are spinning an A, B, and C equally likely events? Why or why not?

11. What fractions of the spins do you expect to land on A? on B? on C?

12. **Writing** Suppose you repeat the experiment 20 times. What results do you expect? Do you think the results will always match your expectations? Why or why not?

13. **Challenge** Sketch a spinner for this situation: The possible outcomes are Red and Green. The probability of spinning Red is three times the probability of spinning Green.

MODULE 2 Quick Quiz

For use after Section 5

1. Evelyn spins the spinner shown 60 times and gets white on 28 spins. What is the experimental probability of getting white?

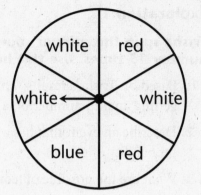

2. Find the theoretical probability of each event.

   a. $P(\text{white})$

   b. $P(\text{red or blue})$

   c. $P(\text{not red})$

3. Suppose you roll three number cubes. List three outcomes that would each produce an odd sum greater than 11.

   Outcome 1: _____, _____, _____   Sum = _____

   Outcome 2: _____, _____, _____   Sum = _____

   Outcome 3: _____, _____, _____   Sum = _____

4. Describe an event that has a probability of

   a. $\frac{1}{2}$

   b. 1

   c. 0

Math Thematics, Book 2
Teacher's Resource Book, Modules 1 and 2

Name _____   Date _____

Practice and Applications
For use after Sections 1–5

For use with Section 1

1. Write each power of ten in standard form.

    a. 10^1 **b.** 10^2 **c.** 10^{-5}

2. Write each power as a fraction with its denominator in standard form.

    a. 3^{-4} **b.** 5^{-3} **c.** 4^{-4}

3. The mean distance from Earth to the sun is 93,000,000 mi. What is this distance in scientific notation?

For use with Section 2

4. Scanning for insects, a bat sends out 400 pulses of sound per second.

    a. Suppose you make a graph with the number of pulses of sound on the vertical axis and the number of seconds on the horizontal axis. What scale would you use for each axis? Explain.

    b. Draw and label a graph of the data.

5. Find the slope of a line with each rise and run.

    a. rise 6   **b.** rise 3   **c.** rise 4
       run 3   run 4   run 16

For use with Section 3

6. a. Sketch the next two shapes in the shape sequence.

    b. How can you find the perimeter of a square from the length of a side?

    c. If the sequence in the table continues, what are the next two terms of the number sequence for the perimeter of each shape?

    (Exercise 6 continues on next page.)

Term number	Shape sequence	Number sequence
1	□	4
2	⊞	8
3	▦	12

Practice and Applications

For use after Sections 1–5

6. d. Write an equation for the perimeter of a square.
Let s = the length of a side of a square. Let P = the
perimeter of the square. Use your equation to find the
perimeter of a square that has sides of length 20 cm.

e. Make a table of values for the first 10 terms of the number
sequence. Use it to make a graph of the sequence. Use your
graph to predict the 15th term of the sequence.

For use with Section 4

7. Katie earns $8 per hour plus $12 for every extra hour she works
over 40 hours per week. If Katie earned $392 last week, how many
extra hours did she work?

8. a. A book states that an average teenager in the United States should
spend at least 130 hours a year exercising. Do you think this is a
reasonable estimate? Explain.

b. What scores would you give your solution in part (a) on the
problem solving and connections scales?

For use with Section 5

9. Suppose a bag contains 12 marbles, with 3 each of the colors red,
yellow, blue, and green. An experiment involves picking a marble
from the bag and putting it back in the bag. Find the theoretical
probability of each event.

a. P(red)   **b.** P(yellow)   **c.** P(not green)

d. P(green or yellow)   **e.** P(not red)   **f.** P(purple)

g. P(blue)   **h.** P(blue or green)   **i.** P(not yellow)

Name _____ Date _____

Test Form A
For use after Module 2

Find the slope of each line.

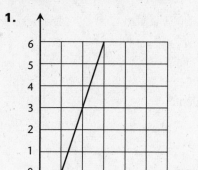

1.

2.

3. Make two line graphs of the data in the table using different vertical or horizontal scales. Label one graph to show that enrollment is decreasing rapidly. Label the other graph to show that enrollment has remained about the same.

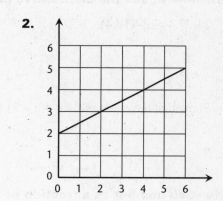

Freemont H.S. Enrollment	
Year	Number of Students
1970	979
1980	987
1990	975
1995	958
2000	926
2004	897

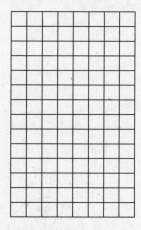 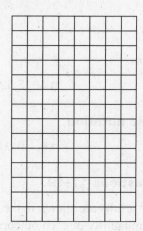

4. **a.** Complete the table for the first 6 terms of the sequence 5, 12, 19, 26, ...

Term Number	1	2	3	4	5	6
Term	5	12	19	26		

b. Write an equation for finding the terms of the sequence.

c. Predict the 150th term of the sequence.

Name _____   Date _____

 **Test Form A**
For use after Module 2

Show how to use the distributive property to evaluate each expression.

5. $24(37.4) - 24(17.4)$

6. $85 \cdot 102$

7. Show that the equations $y = 4(x - 3) + 5$ and $y = 4x - 7$ are equivalent.

Write each number as a fraction or as a mixed number.

8. 0.455

9. 5.44

Replace each blank with >, <, or =.

10. 1.872 ____ 1.89

11. 0.92 ____ 0.100

12. Write 2^{-4} in standard form.

Write each product in standard form.

13. $15.4 \cdot 10^4$

14. $5.32 \cdot 10^{-3}$

Write each each number in scientific notation.

15. 42,003

16. 0.0090

Use the spinner at the right for Questions 17–19.

17. Terry spun the spinner 48 times. Her results are shown in the table below. Find the experimental probability of each outcome.

Outcome	Frequency
blue	20
yellow	12
green	16

18. Find the theoretical probability of each outcome.

19. Suppose you spin the spinner 360 times. About how many times would you expect it to land on blue?

Math Thematics, Book 2
Teacher's Resource Book, Modules 1 and 2

Name _____   Date _____

Find the slope of each line.

1.

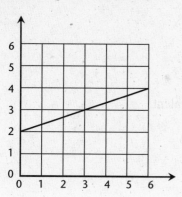

2.

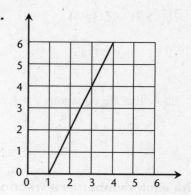

3. Make two line graphs of the data in the table using different vertical or horizontal scales. Label one graph to show that enrollment is decreasing rapidly. Label the other graph to show that enrollment has remained about the same.

Freemont H.S. Enrollment	
Year	Number of Students
1970	875
1980	883
1990	871
1995	854
2000	826
2004	798

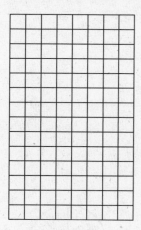 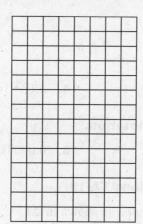

4. **a.** Complete the table for the first 6 terms of the sequence 4, 10, 16, 22, ...

Term Number	1	2	3	4	5	6
Term	4	10	16	22		

b. Write an equation for finding the terms of the sequence.

c. Predict the 150th term of the sequence.

Name _____ Date _____

 **Test Form B**
For use after Module 2

Show how to use the distributive property to evaluate each expression.

5. $16(45.7) - 16(35.7)$

6. $25 \cdot 103$

7. Show that the equations $y = 3(x - 4) + 6$ and $y = 3x - 6$ are equivalent.

Write each number as a fraction or as a mixed number.

8. 0.16

9. 2.018

Replace each blank with >, <, or =.

10. $2.76 \_\_\_\_ 2.759$

11. $0.32 \_\_\_\_ 0.190$

12. Write 2^{-5} in standard form.

Write each product in standard form.

13. $371.4 \cdot 10^2$

14. $6.18 \cdot 10^{-4}$

Write each each number in scientific notation.

15. $67,002$

16. 0.00082

Use the spinner at the right for Questions 17–19.

17. Terry spun the spinner 60 times. Her results are shown in the table below. Find the experimental probability of each outcome.

Outcome	Frequency
blue	12
yellow	34
green	14

18. Find the theoretical probability of each outcome.

19. Suppose you spin the spinner 360 times. About how many times would you expect it to land on blue?

Math Thematics, Book 2
Teacher's Resource Book, Modules 1 and 2

Name _____   Date _____

1. When did the value of the stock decrease?

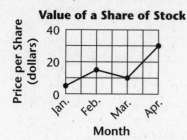

Value of a Share of Stock

Price per Share (dollars)

Month

- **a.** January
- **b.** February
- **c.** March
- **d.** April

2. Which data would be better represented by a line graph than a bar graph?
- **a.** high temperatures in ten cities
- **b.** distances of planets from the sun
- **c.** the weight of a kitten as it grows
- **d.** favorite kinds of ice cream

3. What is the slope of a line with rise 15 and run 20?
- **a.** $\frac{3}{4}$
- **b.** 5
- **c.** $\frac{4}{3}$
- **d.** 1.5

4. Predict the 75th term of the sequence 2, 9, 16, 23, ...
- **a.** 518
- **b.** 520
- **c.** 525
- **d.** 527

5. Write $2 \cdot 2 \cdot 2 \cdot 2$ in exponential form.
- **a.** $4 \cdot 2$
- **b.** 2^4
- **c.** 4^2
- **d.** $4 \cdot 2^4$

6. Anne tosses a coin 80 times and gets heads 45 times. Which of the following expressions represents the experimental probability of getting tails?
- **a.** $80 - 45$
- **b.** $\frac{45}{80}$
- **c.** $\frac{45}{80 - 45}$
- **d.** $\frac{80 - 45}{80}$

7. What is the theoretical probability of this spinner landing on white?

- **a.** $\frac{1}{2}$
- **b.** $\frac{1}{3}$
- **c.** $\frac{1}{4}$
- **d.** $\frac{2}{3}$

8. When n is the term number, which expression describes the nth term of the sequence 6, 12, 24, 48, ... ?
- **a.** $3 \cdot 2^{n-1}$
- **b.** $3 \cdot 2^n$
- **c.** $3 \cdot 2(n-1)$
- **d.** $3 \cdot 2n$

9. Find the slope of the line through these two points.

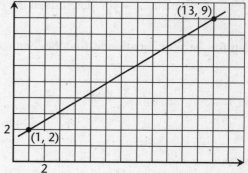

- **a.** 0.48
- **b.** $0.58\overline{3}$
- **c.** 1.2
- **d.** 1.71

10. On Monday, you have quizzes in both math and spelling. You will have a math quiz every 3rd day and a spelling quiz every 4th day. How many times in 50 school days will you have both quizzes on the same day?
- **a.** 3
- **b.** 4
- **c.** 7
- **d.** 12

Name _____   Date _____

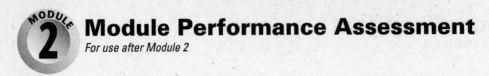

Module Performance Assessment
For use after Module 2

Step 1: Write numbers to represent the first 3 terms of sequence A shown below:

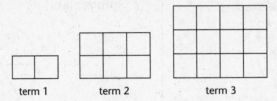

term 1   term 2   term 3

Step 2: Make a table showing the term number, term, and shape sequence
for the first 3 terms of sequence A. Then predict what the 4th and 5th
terms of the sequence will be. Explain your reasoning.

Step 3: Sequence B is defined by the following number pattern: 1, 4, 9, 16,
25, ... Write an equation relating the term number, *n*, with the value
of the term, *t*, for sequence B.

Step 4: Construct a visual representation that compares the first five terms
of sequence A with the first five terms of sequence B. Explain which
type of graph you used and why.

Step 5: Compare the results shown in your graph. Then write an equation
relating the term number, *n*, with the value of the term, *t*, for sequence
A. Explain how you determined the equation.

Step 6: Use your equation to find the 39th term of sequence A.

Name _____   Date _____

Cumulative Test
For use after Modules 1 and 2

For Questions 1–4, use the diagram at the right.

1. Name two acute angles.

2. Name two obtuse angles.

3. Name two right angles.

4. ∠FBE has a measure of 36°.

   a. Find the measure of a complementary angle to ∠FBE.

   b. Find the measure of a supplementary angle to ∠FBE.

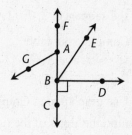

Evaluate each expression. Use the order of operations.

5. $-2 + 14 - 8 + (-5)$ 6. $|-18| - (-3)$ 7. $72 + 8 \div 4 - 3$

8. List the following integers in order from least to greatest.
   $-8, 7, -4, -11, 12, 5, 9, -1$

Graph each ordered pair on the coordinate grid at the right.

9. $(4, 1)$ 10. $(3, -4)$ 11. $(-2, -3)$

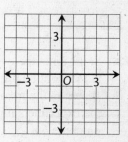

12. Evaluate the expression $-p + 3n$ when $n = 2$ and $p = -5$.

Solve and check.

13. $-89 = x - 31$ 14. $\dfrac{w}{17} = 8$

15. Eric sold 12 subscriptions on the last day of the school fundraiser. That
    brought his total number of subscriptions sold to 54. Write an equation to
    model the situation. Identify the variable you used.

16. Write 5^{-2} as a fraction with its denominator in standard form.

17. Write an inequality statement that uses <, >, or = to compare 5.836 and 5.83492.

Write each number in scientific notation.

18. 0.0023   19. 83,076,000

Cumulative Test
For use after Modules 1 and 2

20. For the sequence: 3, 7, 11, 15, ...

Term Number	1	2	3	4	5	6
Term	3	7	11	15		

    a. Complete the table.

    b. Use graph paper. Graph the points on a coordinate plane.

    c. Find the slope of the line.

    d. Write an equation. Use t for term and n for term number.

    e. Predict the 200th term.

21. Use the distributive property to write an equivalent expression.

    a. $4(w - 6)$ **b.** $15x + 3$

22. Explain how altering the vertical or horizontal axis of a graph can affect the way the displayed data is interpreted by a reader.

23. Sarah spun the two spinners shown at the right 80 times. Her results are shown in the frequency table. Find the experimental probability of each outcome.

Outcome	Frequency
2, 1	18
2, 3	21
4, 1	24
4, 3	17

24. Suppose an experiment consists of spinning each of the two spinners. The resulting numbers are then added.

    a. Complete the table to show the sums (outcomes) that can occur.

    b. Find the theoretical probabilty of each outcome.

    c. If you spun the spinner 90 times, how many times would you expect to get either a 5 or 7?

Spinner A   Spinner B

Spinner A	Spinner B		
	2	4	6
1			
3			
5			

Answer Key

For use before Module 1

Book 2 Pre-Course Test (p. TR-32)

1. 8
2. 20.07
3. 13.5
4. 1.28
5. 2
6. 5
7. 2, 5, 10
8. 5
9. about 1600
10. about 170
11. about 90
12. about 24,000
13. about 8
14. about 81
15. 105
16. 85
17. 364.5
18. 1.89
19. 4.39
20. 22.879
21. 28
22. 16
23. 25
24. >
25. <
26. =
27. $\frac{5}{6}$
28. $\frac{7}{12}$
29. $10\frac{4}{7}$
30.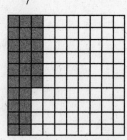

31.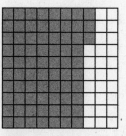

32.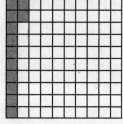

33. −9
34. 11
35. −14
36. 20 cm
37. 23 in.
38. 3
39. 60
40. 2
41. 648
42. $P = 22$ in.; $A = 18$ in.^{2}
43. $P = 24$ m; $A = 35$ m^2
44.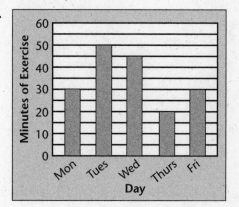

Answer Key

For use before Module 1

45.

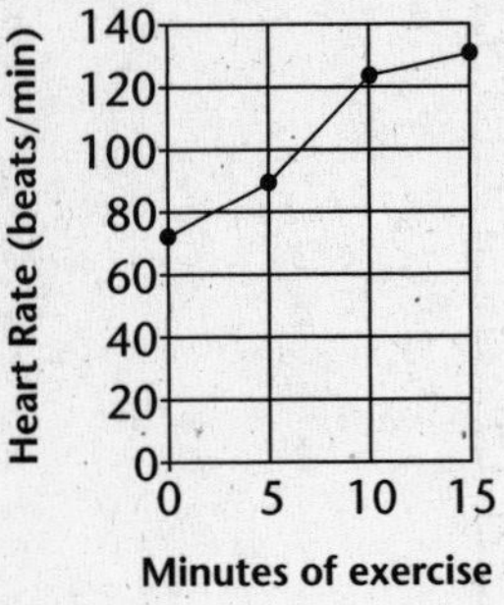

Heart Rate (beats/min)
140
120
100
80
60
40
20
0
0
5
10
15
Minutes of exercise

46. 28

47. 230

Answer Key

For use with Module 1

MODULE 1

Diagnostic Test (p. 1-2)

1. Check students' work; obtuse.
2. D; A
3. C
4. A
5. C
6. B
7. D
8. C
9. A
10. 7
11. 7
12.

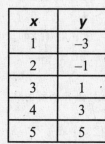
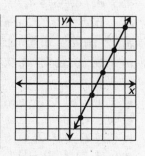

x	y
1	–3
2	–1
3	1
4	3
5	5

13. $34 - 19 = 19 + x - 19,\ 15 = x$
14. $6 \cdot \frac{w}{6} = 1332 \cdot 6,\ w = 792$
15. $k - 9 + 9 = -87 + 9,\ k = -78$
16. Let d = December bill and a = August bill, $d = 3a$

SECTION 1

Practice and Applications (p. 1-12)

1. $\angle ARB, \angle BRS, \angle ARF$
2. $\angle ASE, \angle ASF, \angle ASG$
3. $\angle ARF, \angle RSF$
4. $\angle FSG; 30°$
5. $\angle ASE$ or $\angle ESF$
6. $\angle ESG, 120°; \angle RSG, 150°; \angle BRS, 130°$
7.

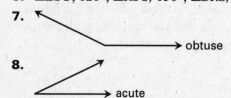

obtuse

8.

acute

9. 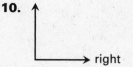 straight
10. 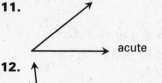 right
11. 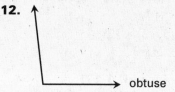 acute
12. 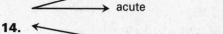 obtuse
13. 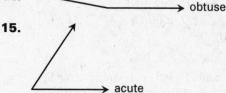 acute
14. obtuse
15. acute

16. **a–d.** 3:00 is a right angle; 7:30 is an acute angle; 6:00 is a straight angle; 5:00 is an obtuse angle.

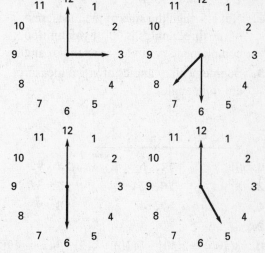

17. 90°
18. **a.** 155° **b.** 65°
19. **a.** 8° **b.** not possible
20. **a.** 108° **b.** 18°
21. **a.** 90° **b.** not possible

22. a. 137° **b.** 47°

23. a. 160° **b.** 70°

24. a. 34° **b.** not possible

25. a. 72° **b.** not possible

26. 43°

27. about 144°

28. a. 16 **b.** 75 **c.** 11 **d.** 150 **e.** 4 **f.** 3.2

29. $3(50) + 3(25) + 8(5) + 4(10) + 2(1) = 307$

30. a. $(25 - 8) \cdot 3 = 51$
   b. $(9 + 9) \div 3 \cdot (5 - 3) = 12$
   c. $(6 \cdot 5) - (5^2 + 2) = 3$

Study Guide Exercises (p. 1-17)

1. $\overrightarrow{PQ}$

2. $\angle BPQ$; 33°

3. $\angle APB$, $\angle QPB$, and $\angle CPB$

4. $\angle APB$, $\angle BPQ$, $\angle QPC$, $\angle APC$, $\angle BPC$, and $\angle APQ$

5. $\angle APQ$ and $\angle CPB$; 120°

6. $\angle APW$ and $\angle WPB$, $\angle APX$ and $\angle XPB$, $\angle APY$ and $\angle YPB$, $\angle APZ$ and $\angle ZPB$

7. $\angle APW$ and $\angle WPX$, $\angle XPY$ and $\angle YPB$, $\angle XPZ$ and $\angle ZPB$, $\angle YPB$ and $\angle WPX$, $\angle APW$ and $\angle XPY$

8. No; although the sum of the measures of the three angles is 90°, by definition complementary angles are pairs of angles.

9. Supplementary angles of equal measure are right angles.

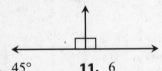

10. 45°   **11.** 6   **12.** 92

13. 8   **14.** 24   **15.** 32

16. 6   **17.** 4   **18.** 9

19. 8

20. $3(100) + 2(50) + 7(10) + 4(5) + 8(1) = 498$

21. $[2^3 + (6^2 - 4^2) \div 4] - 2 \cdot 3 = 7$

Quick Quiz (p. 1-18)

1. $\angle ABE$ and $\angle CBD$

2. Sample Response: $\angle ABC$ and $\angle CBD$

3. 50°; 140°

4.

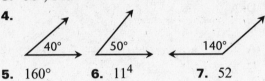

5. 160°   **6.** 11^4 **7.** 52

SECTION 2

Practice and Applications (p. 1-20)

1. a. −8 ft **b.** 966 ft **c.** 60 mi/hr **d.** −480 points

2. a. to the left of −2 **b.** −3, −2, −1 **c.** 1, 2, 3, 4, 5 **d.** −6, −5, −4, −3, −2, −1, 0, 1, 2

3. a. < **b.** > **c.** < **d.** > **e.** > **f.** <

4. a. 12 **b.** −53 **c.** 42 **d.** −26 **e.** 0 **f.** 84

5. a. 8 **b.** 23 **c.** 95 **d.** 95 **e.** 16 **f.** 44

6. a. < **b.** < **c.** >

7. a. J or B **b.** K **c.** vertical **d.** horizontal **e.** one **f.** one

8. a. (3, −2) **b.** (−2, 4) **c.** (2, 3) **d.** (−5, −3) **e.** (−4, 0) **f.** (0, −3)

9. A and G

10. H, I, and K

11.

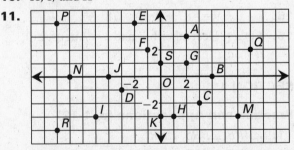

12. Sample Response: Use the lower left corner as the origin, the bottom edge of the table as the horizontal axis, and the left edge of the table as the vertical axis. You cannot do this for a mathematical plane. A mathematical plane extends endlessly in all directions. This means that you must use both positive and negative coordinates.

Answer Key

For use with Module 1

Study Guide Exercises (p. 1-24)

1. >	**2.** >	**3.** >
4. >	**5.** <	**6.** <
7. −5	**8.** 30	**9.** −588
10. 19	**11.** 333	**12.** 8
13. −103	**14.** −22,973	**15.** 10
16. 50	**17.** 2	**18.** 312
19. 6	**20.** 31	**21.** 105
22. 776	**23.** >	**24.** <
25. >	**26.** <	**27.** <
28. >		

29. **a.** A (1, 2), B (2, −2), C (−3, 4), D (−1, −3), E (3, 0)

b–c.

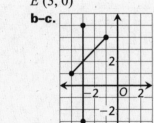

30. **a.** line b **b.** line d **c.** line a, line b, line d

Quick Quiz (p. 1-25)

1. −29°

2. −4, −10, −16

3. −18,942

4. greater than

5.

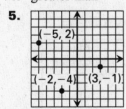

SECTION 3

Practice and Applications (p. 1-31)

1. −4; −6 − (−2) = −4

2. −2; 4 + (−6) = −2

3. −4; 3 − 7 = −4

4. 2; −3 + 5 = 2

5.

$$-4 + 8 = 4$$

6.

$$3 + (-5) = -2$$

7.

$$-2 + (-3) = -5$$

8.

$$0 + (-2) = -2$$

9. −6	**10.** −5	**11.** −9
12. 0	**13.** 6	**14.** −4
15. 6	**16.** −14	**17.** −9

18. −3 + 12 = 9

19. −500 + 900 = 400

20. 250 + 830 + (−1080) = 0

21.

$$-1 - (-6) = 5$$

22.

$$5 - 8 = -3$$

23.

$$-3 - 3 = -6$$

24.

$$2 - (-4) = 6$$

25. −17 + (−2)	**26.** 8 + 4
27. 5 + (−10)	**28.** −15 + 6
29. 30 + (−42)	**30.** −9 + 25
31. −4	**32.** −11

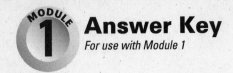

Answer Key

For use with Module 1

33. 9

34. –10

35. –51

36. –14

37. –16

38. –51

39. –3

40. 23

41. 10

42. –13

43. –5952 ft

44. –18 ft

45. 650 points

Study Guide Exercises (p. 1-35)

1. $-7; -5 + (-2) = -7$

2. $-1; 3 - 4 = -1$

3. $1; -1 - (-2) = 1$

4. –6

5. –5

6. 12

7. –31

8. –7

9. 0

10. –5

11. 0

12. 8

13. –14

14. 8

15. –2

16. 8

17. 2

18. 2

19. –2

20. $9 + (-5); 4$

21. $-5 + 8; 3$

22. $0 + 3; 3$

23. $8 + 2; 10$

24. –15

25. –2

26. –10

27. 2

28. –1

Quick Quiz (p. 1-36)

1. **a.** –4 **b.** 0 **c.** –30

2. $2 + 3$

3. **a.** –61 **b.** –5 **c.** –86

4. $-6 + 28 - 35 = -13$

5. Sample Response: 10, –10, –5

Mid-Module Quiz (p. 1-37)

1. Any two of the following: $\overrightarrow{AX}$ or $\overrightarrow{AB}$, $\overrightarrow{BX}$ or $\overrightarrow{BA}$, $\overrightarrow{WX}$ or $\overrightarrow{WY}$, $\overrightarrow{YX}$ or $\overrightarrow{YW}$

2. 130º

3. $\angle AXY$; 50º or $\angle WXB$; 50º

4.

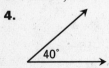

5. 140º

6. –27

7. 13

8. 24

9. 81

10. <

11. >

12. =

13.

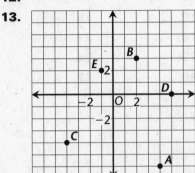

14. $11 + (-18) + 3 = -4$

15. –98

16. –6

17. 11

18. –12

19. 5^4, 625

20. 7^3, 343

21. 25

22. 2

SECTION 4

Practice and Applications (p. 1-45)

1. **a.** 55 mi/hr **b.**

Hours driven	Miles traveled
1	55
2	110
3	165
4	220
5	275

c. $d = 55t$ **d.** 10 hr **e.** Nita's distance from Destin after driving t hours **f.** values from 0 to 10

2. C **3.** A **4.** 50

5. 9 **6.** –8 **7.** 12

Math Thematics, Book 2
Teacher's Resource Book, Modules 1 and 2

Answer Key

For use with Module 1

8. 32 **9.** 33 **10.** 27

11. −33 **12.** −14

13. a. Sample Response: Thomas has q quarters and wants to know how much money he has in all.

b.

q	1	2	3	4
25q	25	50	75	100

14.

x	−2	−1	0	1	2
y	−8	−7	−6	−5	−4

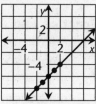

15.

x	−2	−1	0	1	2
y	2	3	4	5	6

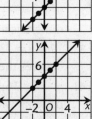

16.

x	−2	−1	0	1	2
y	9	8	7	6	5

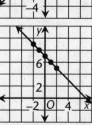

17.

x	−2	−1	0	1	2
y	3	4	5	6	7

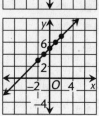

18.

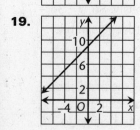

19.

20.

21. a. $80; The point (0, 80) is on each graph. The second coordinate represents the amount of money owed after 0 months, that is, at the time the money was borrowed. **b.** $40; The difference in the second coordinates of (0, 80) and (1, 40) is 40. **c.** $20

d.

Months	Amount Linda owes (dollars)
0	80
1	40
2	0

Months	Amount Mike owes (dollars)
0	80
1	60
2	40
3	20
4	0

e. Linda: $y = 80 − 40x$; x is the number of months since Linda borrowed the money, and y is the amount owed after x months. Mike: $y = 80 − 20x$; x is the number of months since Mike borrowed the money, and y is the amount owed after x months.

22.

x	−4	−2	0	2
y	2	0	−2	−4

; $y = −2 − x$

23.

x	−4	−2	0	2
y	6	8	10	12

; $y = x + 10$

Study Guide Exercises (p. 1-49)

1. B

2. $t + 2$

3. 60

4. −12

5. 15

6. −3

7. −17

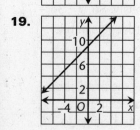

MODULE 1

Answer Key
For use with Module 1

8. 9

9. −4, −3, −2, −1, 0

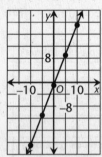

10. −21, −11, −1, 9, 19

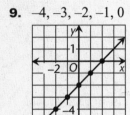

11. Sample Response: Sarah is 4 years younger than Marcia. Marcia is x years old.

x	4	5	6	7	8
y	0	1	2	3	4

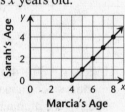

12. a.

d	100	200	300	400	500	600
t	2	4	6	8	10	12

b. $d = 50t$

c.

Visit to Cousins' House

d. 250 mi **e.** Sample Response: I substituted 5 for t in my equation from part (b).

Quick Quiz (p. 1-50)

1. $d + m$

2. 11

3. $c = 5 + 1.5 \cdot n$

4. −5, −2, 1, 4, 7, 10; Check students' graphs.

5. $3 \cdot (x + 15)$

SECTION 5

Practice and Applications (p. 1-52)

1. $6 + x = 10$; x represents the number of problems Sharlene still has to do.

2. $m + 4 = 23$; m represents the number of mineral samples that are not clear quartz.

3. $17 − x = −3$; x represents the number of degrees the temperature dropped.

4. $p − 7 = 36$; p represents the number of patients who originally had appointments.

5. a. $x + 5 = 12$ **b.** Remove 5 tiles from each side; 7

6. a. $m + 4 = 7$ **b.** Remove 4 tiles from each side; 3

7. −61   **8.** 45   **9.** 38

10. 39   **11.** 72   **12.** −67

13. 15   **14.** 4   **15.** 27

16. No.   **17.** Yes.   **18.** Yes.

19. Yes.   **20.** No.   **21.** No.

22. $x + 139 = 180$; x is the measure of the smaller angle; 41.

23. $d + 55 = −63$; d is the original elevation of the submarine; −118.

24. $85 + m = 160$; m is the additional amount of money Andrew needs to have $160; 75.

Study Guide Exercises (p. 1-55)

1. Let s represent the number of subscriptions Dorothy had sold previously. So, $s + 36 = 78$.

2. Let b represent how fast Jacob can bike. So, $b = 5 \cdot 3$.

3. $x + 6 = 9$

4. Sample Response: During the first 5 min of an experiment, the temperature of a chemical solution dropped 4 degrees to 7°C.

If *x* represents the temperature of the solution at the beginning of the experiment, what is the value of *x*?

5. ⊞ + ⊟⊟ = ⊞⊞⊞⊞⊞; $x = 7$
6. −14
7. 11
8. 9
9. 23
10. 32
11. 54
12. −1
13. −4
14. 21
15. 3
16. 12
17. 1
18. Division Property of Equality; 4
19. Division Property of Equality; 5
20. Addition Property of Equality; −11
21. Subtraction Property of Equality; 7
22. Multiplication Property of Equality; 12
23. Division Property of Equality; 6
24. No; substituting 5 for *n* gives −9 + 5, or −4, on the left side, and −4 ≠ 4.

Quick Quiz (p. 1-56)

1. $x + 4 = 10$
2. $n - 14 = 11$, where *n* is the number of students enrolled in the class
3. **a.** $n = 52$ **b.** $r = 92$ **c.** $k = 15$
4. No; $21 - 3 = 18$. The solution is −21.
5. **a.** $82 + d = 180$ **b.** $d = 98$

END-OF-MODULE RESOURCES AND ASSESSMENTS

Practice and Applications, Sections 1–5 (p. 1-57)

1. **a.** 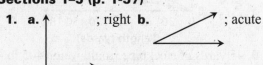 ; right **b.** ; acute

c.  ; obtuse

2. **a.** 105°; 15° **b.** 82°; not possible
   c. 68°; not possible
3. **a.** 26 **b.** 19 **c.** 4900 **d.** 3 **e.** 14 **f.** 5
4. **a.** $(28 - 10) \div 6 = 3$ **b.** $(8 + 2) \cdot 7 = 70$
   c. $(4^2 + 2^2) \div 4 = 5$
5. **a.** 13,804 ft **b.** 0 ft **c.** −8 ft **d.** −282 ft
6. **a.** 0; 0 **b.** −49; 49 **c.** 68; 68
   d. 235; 235 **e.** 99; 99 **f.** −400; 400
7. **a.** > **b.** < **c.** < **d.** > **e.** < **f.** >
8. **a.** −7 **b.** 20 **c.** 33 **d.** 0 **e.** −24 **f.** 34
9. **a.** 3 **b.** 44 **c.** 64 **d.** 68
10. **a.**

x	−10	−5	0	5	10
y	−15	−10	−5	0	5

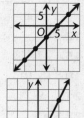

b.

x	−2	−1	0	1	2
y	−3	−1	1	3	5

11. **a.**

t	0	1	2	3	4	5	6
d	0	50	100	150	200	250	300

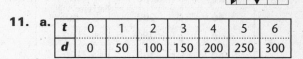

b. $d = 50t$

12. **a.** Let *m* represent the number of marbles that Diana's brother has. So, the equations are $m + 38 = 75$ and $75 - m = 38$. **b.** Let *p* represent the number of points Ramon scored in the game. So, the equations are $5 + p = 23$ and $23 - p = 5$.
13. **a.** 6 **b.** 143 **c.** −36 **d.** −9 **e.** 126 **f.** 12

Test Form A (p. 1-62)

1. ∠AMY, ∠XMH

2. ∠AME, ∠EMH, ∠XMY (any two)

3. ∠AMX, ∠XME, ∠EMY, ∠YMH (any two)

4. **a.** 70° **b.** 160°

5. 1016   6. 3   7. 81

8. −4; positive integers indicate a river level above flood stage, negative integers indicate a river level below flood stage, and zero indicates a river level exactly at flood stage.

9. C   10. C

11. **a–b.** Sample Responses are given.

    a. the blue guidelines for writing on notebook paper **b.** the top and the side of a rectangular door

12. 8   13. −10   14. −25

15. −7   16. (1, 2)   17. (−5, −3)

18. (5, 0)   19. (−3, 3)   20. 11

21. −9   22. 10

23. **a.**

Length (feet)	Weight (pounds)	
	Steel pipe	Plastic tubing
10	50	20
20	100	40
40	200	80
50	250	100
60	300	120
L	5 • L	2 • L

b. steel pipe: $w = 5L$; plastic tubing: $w = 2L$

c.

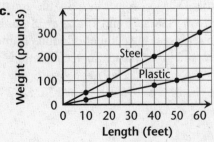

d. 45 feet of steel pipe would weigh 135 lb more than the same length of plastic tubing.

24. 7   25. 75

26. 12   27. −19

28. **a.** $x − 9 = 47$; x represents the number of CDs Elsa originally had. **b.** 56

Test Form B (p. 1-64)

1. ∠AMX, ∠XMC, ∠EMB (any two)

2. ∠AMC, ∠EMC

3. ∠AMB, ∠XME, ∠BMC (any two)

4. **a.** 50° **b.** 140°

5. 73   6. 18   7. 100

8. −7; positive integers indicate a river level above flood stage, negative integers indicate a river level below flood stage, and zero indicates a river level exactly at flood stage.

9. C   10. C

11. **a–b.** Sample Responses are given.

    a. the blue guidelines for writing on notebook paper **b.** the left edge and bottom edge of the paper

12. 1   13. 8   14. −24

15. −4   16. (−1, −2)   17. (5, 3)

18. (−5, 0)   19. (3, −3)   20. 39

21. −40   22. 11

23. **a.**

Length (yards)	Weight (pounds)	
	Steel pipe	Plastic tubing
30	450	180
60	900	360
120	1800	720
150	2250	900
180	2700	1080
L	15L	6L

b. steel pipe: $w = 15L$; plastic tubing: $w = 6L$

c.

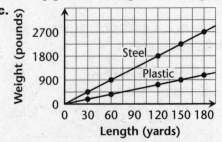

d. 45 yards of steel pipe would weigh 405 lb more than the same length of plastic tubing.

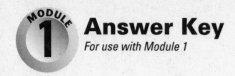

24. 24   **25.** 48

26. 19   **27.** −8

28. **a.** $c - 5 = 39$; c represents the number of cassettes Elsa originally had. **b.** 44

Standardized Test (p. 1-66)

1. a   **2.** d   **3.** c

4. a   **5.** a   **6.** d

7. d   **8.** b   **9.** c

10. c

Performance Assessment (p. 1-67)

Step 1: $6(15) - 175 = -85$

Step 2:

Fundraiser Tickets ($p = 6t - 175$)	
Tickets sold (t)	**Profit (p)**
10	−115
25	−25
150	725

The negative values of p represent losses. The positive values of p represent profits.

Step 3: They must sell 30 or more tickets to make a profit. (See graph with answer to Step 4.)

Step 4: $p = 2t$, where p = profit and t = tickets sold;

Raffle Tickets ($p = 2t$)	
Tickets sold (t)	**Profit (p)**
10	20
25	50
150	300

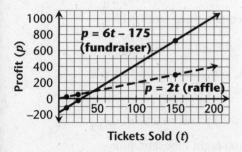

Step 5: If a lot of tickets can be sold, the fundraiser will make more money. But if the potential buying audience is small (< 45), the raffle tickets make more money.

The intersection of the two lines shows that at 45 tickets, both events make exactly the same profit.

Step 6: $n + 26 = 300$, where n is the number of raffle tickets sold;

$$n + 26 = 300$$
$$n = 300 - 26$$
$$n = 274$$

274 tickets have been sold.

MODULE 2

Diagnostic Test (p. 2-2)

1. C **2.** B **3.** A

4. D **5.** B

6.

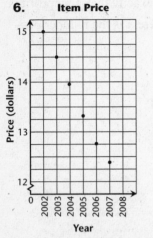 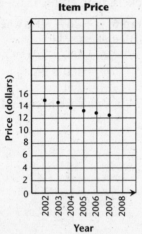

7. a.

Term Number	1	2	3	4	5	6
Term	3	7	11	15	19	23

b. $t = 4n - 1$, where t is the term and n is the term number. **c.** 395

8. C **9.** A

10. Make a Plan, Carry Out the Plan, Look Back

11. blue: $\frac{25}{39}$, yellow: $\frac{9}{39}$ or $\frac{3}{13}$, green: $\frac{5}{39}$

12. blue: $\frac{4}{6}$ or $\frac{2}{3}$, yellow: $\frac{1}{6}$, green: $\frac{1}{6}$

13. about 133 times

SECTION 1

Practice and Applications (p. 2-11)

1. a. three thousand, two hundred eighty-four and fifteen hundredths **b.** eight hundred thirty-five thousandths **c.** five and twenty-five thousandths **d.** two and three thousandths **e.** one hundred three ten-thousandths **f.** ten and sixty-one thousandths **g.** two hundred five hundred-thousandths **h.** five and one ten-thousandth **i.** thirty-one and five hundred two thousandths

2. a. $\frac{73}{100}$ **b.** $41\frac{9}{10}$ **c.** $\frac{305}{1000}$ **d.** $\frac{63}{10,000}$ **e.** $1\frac{71}{10,000}$

f. $4\frac{36,005}{100,000}$ **g.** $6\frac{804}{10,000}$ **h.** $12\frac{1012}{100,000}$

i. $18\frac{26}{100,000}$ **j.** $\frac{2}{1000}$ **k.** $\frac{18}{100}$ **l.** $14\frac{6}{10}$

m. $2\frac{125}{1000}$ **n.** $3\frac{5}{100}$ **o.** $10\frac{105}{1000}$ **p.** $6\frac{50}{100}$

q. $9\frac{4}{10}$ **r.** $7\frac{225}{1000}$

3. a. > **b.** > **c.** < **d.** < **e.** = **f.** < **g.** > **h.** < **i.** > **j.** < **k.** > **l.** > **m.** = **n.** > **o.** <

4. a. 0.521, 0.457, 0.459, 0.5, 0.508, 0.52, 0.46, 0.533 **b.** 0.457, 0.459, 0.46, 0.5, 0.508, 0.52, 0.521, 0.533

5. a. 1000 **b.** 100,000 **c.** 1 **d.** 0.01 **e.** 10,000 **f.** 0.001 **g.** 1,000,000 **h.** 0.0001 **i.** 0.1

6. a. $\frac{1}{32}$ **b.** $\frac{1}{64}$ **c.** $\frac{1}{8}$ **d.** $\frac{1}{216}$ **e.** $\frac{1}{225}$ **f.** $\frac{1}{27,000}$

7. a. 10^7 **b.** 10^{-1} **c.** 10^3 **d.** 10^{-5} **e.** 10^0 **f.** 10^{-3}

8. a. 46,000 **b.** 0.001635 **c.** 14,241.3 **d.** 34,700 **e.** 35.1 **f.** 0.231467 **g.** 6.215 **h.** 5.20 **i.** 0.0000241

9. a. $1.6302 \cdot 10^4$ **b.** $4.7 \cdot 10^{-3}$ **c.** $6.3257 \cdot 10^3$ **d.** $2.416 \cdot 10^{-1}$ **e.** $6.241 \cdot 10^5$ **f.** $5.8 \cdot 10^{-5}$

10. a. 7899.8 mi; 7917.52 mi **b.** mean diameter

Study Guide Exercises (p. 2-15)

1. twenty-seven thousandths; $\frac{27}{1000}$

2. fifteen and five hundred fifty-one thousandths; $15\frac{551}{1000}$

3. twenty-three and one thousand ninety-nine ten-thousandths; $23\frac{1099}{10,000}$

4. eighteen and three tenths; $18\frac{3}{10}$

5. eighty-nine hundredths; $\frac{89}{100}$

6. one and one hundred thirty-three millionths; $1\frac{133}{1,000,000}$

7. forty-two and seven tenths; $42\frac{7}{10}$

8. sixty and eight thousand nine ten-thousandths; $60\frac{8009}{10,000}$

Math Thematics, Book 2
Teacher's Resource Book, Modules 1 and 2

9. <
10. >
11. >
12. >
13. >
14. =
15. 0.00001
16. 1
17. 10,000
18. 0.01
19. 10,000,000,000
20. $\frac{1}{125}$
21. $\frac{1}{7}$
22. $\frac{1}{64}$
23. $\frac{1}{243}$
24. $\frac{1}{16}$
25. $\frac{1}{5^8}$
26. $\frac{1}{7^3}$
27. $\frac{1}{14^2}$
28. $\frac{1}{10^4}$
29. $\frac{1}{6^6}$
30. 270,000
31. 0.002519
32. 99
33. 36.1
34. 0.000045
35. 12,768
36. $4.512 \cdot 10^3$
37. $3.05 \cdot 10^{-2}$
38. $5.6983 \cdot 10^4$
39. $5.69 \cdot 10^1$
40. $9 \cdot 10^{-3}$
41. $1.5205 \cdot 10^1$
42. $1.117 \cdot 10^{-1}$
43. $6.71006 \cdot 10^4$

Quick Quiz (p. 2-16)

1. $2\frac{34}{1000}$
2. 2.39; 0.390 > 0.389
3. 70,200
4. a. $\frac{1}{5^3}$ b. $\frac{1}{125}$
5. $9.45 \cdot 10^7$
6. a. 0.00083 b. 704.5
7. 1

SECTION 2

Practice and Applications (p. 2–19)

1. a. 107 to 55, $\frac{107}{55}$, 107 : 55; b. 2
2. a.

m	t
170	144.5
180	153
190	161.5
200	170

    b.

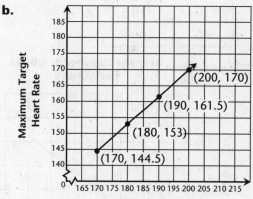

    c. about 176 beats per minute
3. a. $\frac{1}{2}$ b. 3 c. $\frac{1}{3}$ d. $\frac{2}{3}$
4. a. 2 b. 3 c. $\frac{3}{4}$ d. 1 e. 3 f. $\frac{2}{5}$ g. $\frac{1}{3}$ h. $\frac{1}{2}$
    i. $\frac{4}{5}$
5. a. Rachel's performance did not change from Week 2 to Week 3. b. It took Rachel less time to run the race as the season progressed; therefore, her performance improved. c. The vertical scale could have smaller intervals.

(Answer to 5(c) is continued on next page.)

This would draw attention to Rachel's improvement, as running even a few seconds more quickly is significant to the race.

6. **a.** Sample Response: about 40 words/min
   b. Sample Response: about 50 words/min
   c. Yes; Sample Response: It looks as if Clark types much faster than Jenny. In fact, Jenny types faster than Clark. Check students' work.

Study Guide Exercises (p. 2-23)

1. 3 to 4; $\frac{3}{4}$

2. 91 : 34; $\frac{91}{34}$

3. 27 to 100; 27 : 100

4. 9 : 1; $\frac{9}{1}$

5.

m	b
10	150
20	300
30	450
40	600

6.

Average Number of Blinks per Minute

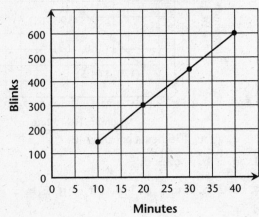

7. 375 times

8. $\frac{1}{2}$, or 0.5

9. $\frac{1}{3}$, or $0.\overline{3}$

10. 3

11. 8

12. $\frac{3}{5}$, or 0.6

13.

Average Daily Temperatures Madrid, Spain

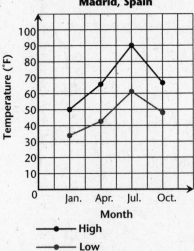

14. The average high and low temperatures increase from January to July. The increase between April and July is steeper than the increase between January and April. The temperatures decrease between July and October.

15. The difference between the high and low temperatures stays about the same throughout the year.

16. Sample Response: to decide what time of year to visit Madrid

17. Check students' work.

18. Sample Response: Use the graph whose line has a smaller slope because it will make your increase in hourly pay appear less significant.

Quick Quiz (p. 2-24)

1.

Calories Burned in 15 Minutes of Downhill Skiing	
Body Weight (lb)	**Calories Burned**
100	45
125	56.25
150	67.5
175	78.75

2. As the body weight increases, the number of Calories burned increases at a constant rate. The data would show a straight line on a graph whose points represent a linear function.

3. 2

4. $\frac{1}{3}$

Mid-Module Quiz (p. 2-25)

1. 0.234, 0.7, 1.336, 1.35

2. $\frac{1}{81}$

3. 6,278,000

4. $6.4 \cdot 10^4$

5. $3.5 \cdot 10^{-4}$

6.

m	C
0	$10
25	$13.75
80	$22
150	$32.50

7. As the number of minutes increases, the cost increases at a constant rate. The data would show a straight line on a graph whose points represent a linear function.

8. $\frac{6}{3} = 2$

9. Sample Responses are given.

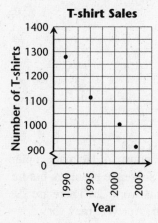

T-shirt Sales

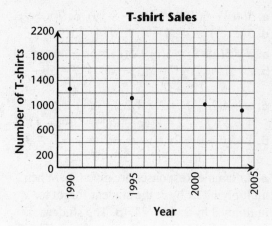

T-shirt Sales

SECTION 3

Practice and Applications (p. 2-31)

1. Each term in the number sequence gives the number of squares in the corresponding term of the shape sequence.

2. a. 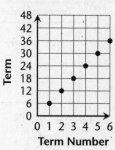 **b.** 10

3. a. Sample Response: Add 2 squares to the top row of the preceding term. **b.** 12 **c.** 20; 180

4. a. $t = 7n$ **b.** $t = n - 2$ **c.** $t = n + 6$ **d.** $t = \frac{n}{4}$

5. a.

Term number	Term
1	6
2	12
3	18
4	24
5	30
6	36

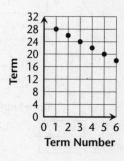

$t = 6n$; 60

b.

Term number	Term
1	28
2	26
3	24
4	22
5	20
6	18

$t = 30 - 2n$; 10

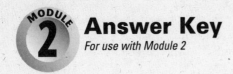
6. a. $5(40) + 5(7)$ **b.** $8(2x) + 8(16)$ **c.** $9(8 + 9)$
d. $3(x - 5)$ **e.** $4x(1 + 4)$ **f.** $x(14) - x(9)$

7. a. $d = 5(c + 8) = 5(c) + 5(8) = 5c + 40$
b. $t = x(5 + 7) - 7 = x(5) + x(7) - 7 = 5x + 7x - 7 = 12x - 7$
c. $w = 4(2z - 1) + 2 = 4(2z) - 4(1) + 2 = 8z - 4 + 2 = 8z - 2 = 2(4z) - 2(1) = 2(4z - 1)$
d. $x = (y - 3) + 2y = y - 3 + 2y = y + 2y - 3 = 3y - 3 = 3(y) - 3(1) = 3(y - 1)$

8. a–d. Sample Responses are given. **a.** When multiplying $2x$ by 3, the student forgot to multiply 3 by 2; $6x + 24$. **b.** The student forgot to multiply 7 by 7; $49t + 49$. **c.** The student combined two terms that were not like; $5n + 25$. **d.** The student distributed the 6 to the 3, which was not in the parentheses; $6y + 15$.

9. a. Sample Response: $0.75(2 + 3)$; $2(0.75) + 3(0.75)$ **b.** $3.75 **c.** Check students' work.

Study Guide Exercises (p. 2-35)

1. $t = 4n$

2. $t = n - 2$

3. $t = 6 + 2n$ or $t = 2n + 6$

4.

Sequence Table	
Term number	**Term**
1	6
2	12
3	18
4	24

Sequence Graph:

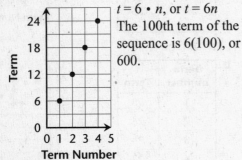

Sequence Equation:
$t = 6 \cdot n$, or $t = 6n$
The 100th term of the sequence is $6(100)$, or 600.

5. **6.** $7(p - 5)$ **7.** $9(10 + 1)$

8. $x(17 + 6)$ **9.** $61(7) - 8(7)$

10. 1728; Sample Response: $6(6) \cdot 6(8)$

11. 1568; Sample Response: $14(1) \cdot 14(8)$

12. 3600; Sample Response: $10(3) \cdot 10(12)$

13. 27 **14.** 15 **15.** 80

16. a. Sample Responses: $2(16 \cdot 8) + 2(11 \cdot 8)$; $16(16 + 11)$ **b.** $1620 **c.** Check students' work.

Quick Quiz (p. 2-36)

1. $t = 5n + 2$

2. a.

Sequence Table	
Term number	**Term**
1	5
2	11
3	17
4	23
5	29
6	35

b. Sequence Graph

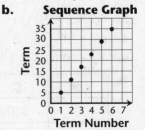

c. $t + 6n - 1$, where t is the term and n is the term number. **d.** 1199

3. a. $5(m) + 5(11)$ or $5m + 55$ **b.** $4(x - 3)$

4. $(x - 7) + 2x = 3x - 21 + 2x = (3x + 2x) + (-21) = 5x + (-21) = 5x - 21$

SECTION 4

Practice and Applications (p. 2-40)

1. a. 6 min **b.** 150 min

2. 32 sales

3. 32 in.

4. 2 horses

5. 99

6. October

7. 123 parents

8. 4 boards

9. a. Sample Response: 4; He made a plan and used it to solve the problem, but he didn't verify his work. **b.** There are 29 squares; no. **c.** Answers may vary.

10. a. 3 quarters, 3 dimes, and 3 pennies or 1 quarter, 8 dimes, and 3 pennies **b.** Answers may vary.

Answer Key

For use with Module 2

11. **a.** 2 mysteries, 2 fantasy books, and 1 of each of the other books **b.** Answers may vary.

Study Guide Exercises (p. 2-46)

1. 4 min
2. 5400 words
3. $33\frac{1}{3}$ hr
4. No; both methods of payment would have a ratio of $1 per 180 words.
5. 44 people
6. 4 times (on the 6th, 12th, 18th, and 24th days after today)
7. A and B; Check students' work.
8. Sample Response: 1; I did not understand the problem well enough to get started.
9. Sample Response: 3; I understood the problem well enough to make a plan and use it, but not well enough to extend the solution to other cases.
10. 11; Sample Response: The numbers in the pattern are modeled by the equation $n = 2t + 1$, where n = the number and t = the position of the number; the 200th number is $2(200) + 1$, or 401; I would rate my work a 5 on the scale.

Quick Quiz (p. 2-47)

1. Sample Response: First decide what kinds of clothing students want to buy. Get prices from the manufacturer. Conduct a student poll. Determine the fraction of students who wish to purchase each item. Use guess and check to find the numbers of each type of clothing you can buy that are in the same proportions as student poll numbers with a total price below $1000. For example, one fourth of students want hats, one half sweatshirts, and one fourth T-shirts. Estimate how much it would cost to buy 25 hats, 50 sweatshirts, and 25 T-shirts. Revise estimate and check again.

2. The student solved the problem correctly but did not make any connections with other types of problems.

3. 36

4. **a.** 3, 2, 2, 3; 36; if you multiply the numbers of choices per category together, you get the number of combinations. **b.** 24,000

SECTION 5

Practice and Applications (p. 2-53)

1. **a–d.** Answers may vary.
2. **a.** $\frac{16}{38}$ or $\frac{8}{19}$ **b.** Sample Response: The spinner stops on a number less than 8; the spinner stops on a number greater than 8.
3. 1, 2, 3, 4, 5, or 6
4. Answers may vary, but the experimental probability for both outcomes should be about $\frac{1}{2}$.
5. **a–d.** Sample Responses are given. **a.** 4 and 6, 3 and 5, 2 and 4 **b.** 4 and 4, 3 and 3, 2 and 2 **c.** 3 and 5, 4 and 4, 2 and 6 **d.** 2 and 4, 2 and 6, 1 and 3
6. **a.** $\frac{24}{100}$ or $\frac{6}{25}$ **b.** $\frac{30}{100}$ or $\frac{3}{10}$ **c.** $\frac{26}{100}$ or $\frac{13}{50}$ **d.** $\frac{20}{100}$ or $\frac{1}{5}$ **e.** $\frac{80}{100}$ or $\frac{4}{5}$ **f.** $\frac{50}{100}$ or $\frac{1}{2}$ **g.** $\frac{76}{100}$ or $\frac{19}{25}$ **h.** $\frac{0}{100}$ or 0
7. $\frac{1}{6}, \frac{1}{6}, \frac{1}{6}$
8.

	Spinner 1			
Spinner 2	**1**	**2**	**3**	**4**
1	2	3	4	5
2	3	4	5	6
3	4	5	6	7
4	5	6	7	8
5	6	7	8	9
6	7	8	9	10

a. $\frac{1}{24}$ **b.** $\frac{4}{24}$ or $\frac{1}{6}$ **c.** 0 **d.** $\frac{3}{24}$ or $\frac{1}{8}$ **e.** $\frac{2}{24}$ or $\frac{1}{12}$ **f.** $\frac{4}{24}$ or $\frac{1}{6}$ **g.** $\frac{7}{24}$ **h.** $\frac{12}{24}$ or $\frac{1}{2}$ **i.** 0

9. **a.** A, B **b.** No; A covers a larger area. **c.** $\frac{2}{3}, \frac{1}{3}$; The area covered by A is twice that covered by B. **d.** Sample Response: A: 20; B: 10; No; theoretical and experimental probabilities are usually not the same.

10. a. 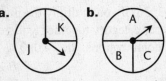 **b.**

Study Guide Exercises (p. 2-57)

1. $\frac{15}{25}$ or $\frac{3}{5}$

2. Sample Responses: P(spinning a number less than 5) = 1; P(spinning a 5) = 0

3. 1, 2, 3, 4, 5, 6

4. Check students' work.

5. $\frac{1}{4}$

6. $\frac{1}{4}$

7. $\frac{1}{2}$

8. $\frac{1}{2}$

9. A, B, C

10. No; the three sectors are not the same size.

11. $\frac{1}{4}, \frac{1}{2}, \frac{1}{4}$

12. Sample Response: Spin A about 5 times, B about 10 times, and C about 5 times. No; theoretical and experimental probabilities are often not the same.

13.

Quick Quiz (p. 2-58)

1. $\frac{28}{60}$ or $\frac{7}{15}$

2. a. $\frac{3}{6}$ or $\frac{1}{2}$ **b.** $\frac{3}{6}$ or $\frac{1}{2}$ **c.** $\frac{4}{6}$ or $\frac{2}{3}$

3. Sample Response: 3, 5, 5; 3, 4, 6; 4, 4, 5

4. Sample Responses using a number cube labeled 1–6: **a.** rolling an even number **b.** rolling a number less than 10 **c.** rolling a number greater than 6

END-OF-MODULE RESOURCES AND ASSESSMENTS

Practice and Applications, Sections 1–5 (p. 2-59)

1. a. 10 **b.** 100 **c.** 0.00001

2. a. $\frac{1}{81}$ **b.** $\frac{1}{125}$ **c.** $\frac{1}{256}$

3. $9.3 \cdot 10^6$

4. a. Sample Responses: horizontal axis: 0, 1, 2, 3, 4, …; vertical axis: 0, 400, 800, 1200, …

b.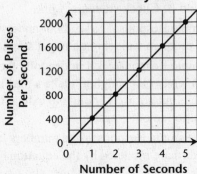

5. a. 2 **b.** $\frac{3}{4}$ **c.** $\frac{1}{4}$

6. a. 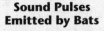 **b.** perimeter = 4 • length

c. 16, 20 **d.** $P = 4s$; 80 cm **e.** For the table and graph, check students' work; 60

7. 6 hr

8. a. Yes; if a teenager exercises about $2\frac{1}{2}$ hr a week, then the teenager will exercise about 130 hr in a year. **b.** Answers may vary.

9. a. $\frac{3}{12}$ or $\frac{1}{4}$ **b.** $\frac{3}{12}$ or $\frac{1}{4}$ **c.** $\frac{9}{12}$ or $\frac{3}{4}$ **d.** $\frac{6}{12}$ or $\frac{1}{2}$

e. $\frac{9}{12}$ or $\frac{3}{4}$ **f.** 0 **g.** $\frac{3}{12}$ or $\frac{1}{4}$ **h.** $\frac{6}{12}$ or $\frac{1}{2}$

i. $\frac{9}{12}$ or $\frac{3}{4}$

MODULE 2 Answer Key

For use with Module 2

Test Form A (p. 2-61)

1. $\frac{3}{1}$ or 3

2. $\frac{1}{2}$ or 0.5

3. Sample Response:

4. a.

Term Number	1	2	3	4	5	6
Term	5	12	19	26	33	40

b. $t = 7n - 2$, where t is the term and n is the term number. **c.** 1048

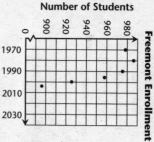

Number of Students

Freemont Enrollment

5. $24(37.4 - 17.4) = 24(20)$
   $= 480$

6. $85(100 + 2) = 85(100) + 85(2)$
   $= 8500 + 170$
   $= 8670$

7. $y = 4(x) - 4(3) + 5$
   $y = 4x - 12 + 5$
   $y = 4x + (-12 + 5)$
   $y = 4x + (-7)$ is the same as $y = 4x - 7$

8. $\frac{455}{1000}$

9. $5\frac{44}{100}$

10. $<$

11. $>$

12. $\frac{1}{16}$

13. 154,000

14. 0.00532

15. $4.20G3 \cdot 10^4$

16. $9 \cdot 10^{-3}$

17. blue: $\frac{20}{48}$ or $\frac{5}{12}$; yellow: $\frac{12}{48}$ or $\frac{1}{4}$; green: $\frac{16}{48}$ or $\frac{1}{3}$

18. blue: $\frac{4}{6}$ or $\frac{2}{3}$; yellow: $\frac{1}{6}$; green: $\frac{1}{6}$

19. 240

Test Form B (p. 2-63)

1. $\frac{1}{3}$

2. $\frac{2}{1}$ or 2

3. Sample Response:

4. a.

Term Number	1	2	3	4	5	6
Term	4	10	16	22	28	34

b. $t = 6n - 2$, where t is the term and n is the term number. **c.** 898

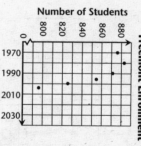

Number of Students

Freemont Enrollment

Number of Students

Freemont Enrollment

5. $16(45.7 - 35.7) = 16(10)$
   $= 160$

6. $25(100 + 3) = 25(100) + 25(3)$
   $= 2500 + 75$
   $= 2575$

7. $y = 3(x) - 3(4) + 6$
   $y = 3x - 12 + 6$
   $y = 3x + (-12 + 6)$
   $y = 3x + -6$ is the same as $y = 3x - 6$

8. $\frac{16}{100}$

9. $2\frac{18}{1000}$

10. $>$

11. $>$

12. $\frac{1}{32}$

13. 37,140

14. 0.000618

15. $6.7002 \cdot 10^4$

16. $8.2 \cdot 10^{-4}$

17. blue: $\frac{12}{60}$ or $\frac{1}{5}$; yellow: $\frac{34}{60}$ or $\frac{17}{30}$; green: $\frac{14}{60}$ or $\frac{7}{30}$

18. blue: $\frac{2}{8}$ or $\frac{1}{4}$; yellow: $\frac{4}{8}$ or $\frac{2}{2}$; green: $\frac{2}{8}$ or $\frac{1}{4}$

19. 90

Standardized Test (p. 2-65)

1. c
2. c
3. a
4. b
5. b
6. d
7. b
8. b
9. b
10. b

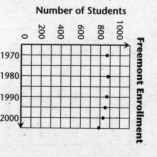

Performance Assessment (p. 2-66)

Step 1: 2, 6, 12, …

Step 2:

Term number	1	2	3	4	5
Term value	2	6	12	?	?
Shape sequence	□ (1×2)	▦ (2×3)	▦ (3×4)	?	?

Using the progression of shape sequences shown in the table, the 4th and 5th terms can be predicted. The 4th and 5th shapes will be 4×5 and 5×6, so the 4th term = 20 and the 5th term = 30.

Step 3: $t = n^2$

Step 4: Graph sequences A and B on the same coordinate grid to compare the sequences, as shown below.

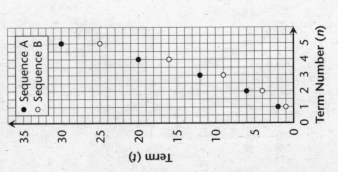

Step 5: By comparing terms with the same term number in the graph for sequences A and B, one can see that the value of each term of sequence A is greater than the corresponding term of sequence B by the amount of the term number. Term 1 of sequence A is 1 greater than term 1 of sequence B; term 2 of sequence A is 2 greater than term 2 of sequence B, and so on. Since the equation for sequence B is $t = n^2$, where t is the term and n is the term number, the equation for sequence A is $t = n^2 + n$, where t is the term and n is the term number.

Step 6: $39^2 + 39 = 1521 + 39 = 1560$

Answer Key
For use after Modules 1 and 2

Modules 1 and 2 Cumulative Test (p. CT-1)

1. Any two of the following: $\angle GAB$, $\angle ABE$, $\angle EBD$

2. $\angle CBE$, $\angle GAF$

3. $\angle CBD$, $\angle DBA$

4. **a.** $54°$ **b.** $144°$

5. -1

6. 21

7. 71

8. $-11, -8, -4, -1, 5, 7, 9, 12$

9–11.
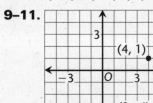

12. 11

13. -58

14. 136

15. $m + 12 = 54$, where m is the number of subscriptions he had sold before the last day.

16. $\dfrac{1}{25}$

17. $5.836 > 5.83492$

18. $2.3 \cdot 10^{-3}$

19. $8.3076 \cdot 10^{7}$

20. **a.**

Term number	Term
1	3
2	7
3	11
4	15
5	19
6	23

b.
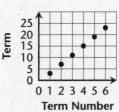

c. 4 **d.** $t = 4n - 1$, where t is the term and n is the term number. **e.** 799

21. **a.** $4w - 24$ **b.** $3(5x + 1)$

22. Sample Response: By using smaller increments when numbering the y-axis, the data in the graph can be made to appear to be drastically increasing or decreasing over time. If the increments on the y-axis are greater, the changes from one data point to another may not be so noticeable, giving the reader the impression that the increase, decrease, or changes are not very significant.

23. $P(2, 1) = \dfrac{18}{80}$ or $\dfrac{9}{40}$, $P(2, 3) = \dfrac{21}{80}$, $P(4, 1) = \dfrac{3}{10}$, $P(4, 3) = \dfrac{17}{80}$

24. **a.**

Spinner A	Spinner B 2	4	6
1	3	5	7
3	5	7	9
5	7	9	11

b. $P(3) = \dfrac{1}{9}$, $P(5) = \dfrac{2}{9}$, $P(7) = \dfrac{1}{3}$, $P(9) = \dfrac{2}{9}$, $P(11) = \dfrac{1}{9}$

c. 50 times